'*Eat Like the Animals* is a wonderfully clever and unusual introduction to the science of healthy eating. I loved the way it was written, and I found it full of drama, insight and surprise. Raubenheimer and Simpson make a very compelling case for the importance of protein in regulating our hunger, and very powerfully demonstrate the horrific role that the junk food industry has played in our lives. Essential reading'

Dr Michael Mosley, science presenter
and author of The Fast 800

'At last a book on diet and nutrition that makes sense. In a world awash with misinformation about what and when to eat, *Eat Like the Animals* is a breath of fresh air. I couldn't put it down. Based on more than 30 years of cutting-edge research, it explains how the modern food environment hacks our hunger control system then explains what we all should be eating to live healthily and age well'

David Sinclair, Professor of Genetics and co-Director
of the Paul F. Glenn Center for the Biology of Aging,
Harvard Medical School and author of
Lifespan: Why We Age—and Why We Don't Have To

'*Eat Like the Animals* is quite simply a masterpiece. I am completely blown away by the science and enthralled by the clarity and elegance of the writing. Raubenheimer and Simpson have revealed the deep evolutionary secrets of the most important physiological need any animal faces by asking the right questions, and have eviscerated all the charlatans, quacks and pseudoscientists who seek fame and fortune by peddling rubbish. The story the authors have told is very important—more so than many people will realise'

Dr George McGavin,
zoologist and broadcaster

'*Eat Like the Animals* is a must-read. This beautifully written book proposes a highly original and compelling explanation for why so many of us gain weight in today's over-processed food environment. Raubenheimer and Simpson are biologists who use their deep knowledge of animal and insect physiology, evolution, and feeding behavior to construct a compelling hypothesis: we share with animals an innate appetite for protein that regulates what we eat'

Marion Nestle, Professor of Nutrition,
Food Studies, and Public Health, Emerita,
New York University, and author of Unsavory Truth

DAVID RAUBENHEIMER is the Leonard P. Ullman Professor of Nutritional Ecology in the School of Life and Environmental Sciences, and Nutrition Theme Leader in the Charles Perkins Centre at the University of Sydney. He previously spent 17 years at Oxford, initially as a doctoral student then as a Research Fellow and Departmental Lecturer in Zoology and Fellow of Magdalen College. He heads the Sydney Food and Nutrition Network, and is a member of the Australian National Committee for Nutrition.

STEPHEN J. SIMPSON is Academic Director of the Charles Perkins Centre and Professor in the School of Life and Environmental Sciences at the University of Sydney. He spent 22 years at Oxford University before returning to Australia in 2005. He is a Fellow of the Royal Society of London, a Companion in the Order of Australia and has been prominent in the media having presented *Great Southern Land* for ABC TV.

EAT LIKE THE ANIMALS

What nature teaches us about the science of healthy eating

David Raubenheimer & Stephen J. Simpson

HarperCollins*Publishers*

HarperCollins*Publishers*

First published in the USA in 2020
by Houghton Mifflin Harcourt
First published in the UK in 2020
by William Collins
First published in Australia in 2020
by HarperCollinsPublishers Australia Pty Limited
ABN 36 009 913 517
harpercollins.com.au

HarperCollins*Publishers*
Level 13, 201 Elizabeth Street, Sydney NSW 2000, Australia
Unit D1, 63 Apollo Drive, Rosedale, Auckland 0632, New Zealand
A 53, Sector 57, Noida, UP, India
1 London Bridge Street, London, SE1 9GF, United Kingdom
Bay Adelaide Centre, East Tower, 22 Adelaide Street West, 41st floor, Toronto, Ontario M5H 4E3, Canada
195 Broadway, New York NY 10007, USA

A catalogue record for this book is available from
the National Library of Australia

ISBN 978 1 4607 5869 4 (paperback)
ISBN 978 1 4607 1247 4 (ebook)

Cover design: Design by Committee
Cover images by shutterstock.com
Printed and bound in Australia by McPherson's Printing Group
The papers used by HarperCollins in the manufacture of this book are a natural, recyclable product made from wood grown in sustainable plantation forests. The fibre source and manufacturing processes meet recognised international environmental standards, and carry certification

Contents

To Jacqueline, Gabriel, Julian, Jan, and Fred

—DR

To Lesley, Alastair, Nick, and Jen

—SJS

Introduction

Stella lived in a community on the outskirts of Cape Town, South Africa. She was one of twenty-five adults who between them had an impressive forty children. It was a serene setting on the foothills of Table Mountain, surrounded by vineyards, pine plantations, groves of eucalyptus trees, stretches of natural fynbos vegetation, and a few suburban settlements.

Caley Johnson was a young anthropology student from New York City. Her graduate thesis was on nutrition of a rural population in Uganda, who lived almost entirely off natural foods. Her advisors suggested that it would be an interesting comparison to include in the study a population that ate not only natural foods but also some sugary and fatty processed foods. This is what brought Caley to Cape Town, where she and Stella met.

Caley's research approach, standard for her field, involves watching individuals throughout an entire day and recording which foods they eat and how much of each. The foods are then analyzed in a laboratory for their nutrient content to give a detailed daily record of the diet. But this study was radical in one respect: rather than follow several subjects, each on a separate day, the team had decided to study the diet of only one individual for thirty consecutive days. Caley therefore came to know Stella and her eating habits intimately.

What she saw was intriguing. Stella's diet was surprisingly diverse: she ate many foods, almost ninety different things over thirty days, and on each day, she ate different combinations of natural and processed foods. This suggested that Stella was not particularly discerning, indiscriminately eating whatever she fancied. The numbers from the nutrient laboratory appeared to tell the same story. The ratio of fats to carbohydrates in Stella's diet varied widely, as might be expected given the variety of foods that she ate and how these differed from one day to the next.

Then Caley noticed something unexpected. When she totaled the combined calories from carbs and fats each day and plotted that figure on a graph against the amount of protein consumed each day, there was a tight relationship. This meant that the ratio of protein to fats and carbs—a very important measure of dietary balance—had remained absolutely consistent over the course of an entire month, regardless of what Stella had eaten. What's more, the ratio that Stella had eaten each day—one part protein to five parts fats and carbs combined—was the same combination that had been proven to be nutritionally balanced for a healthy female of Stella's size. Far from being indiscriminate, Stella was a meticulously precise eater who knew which dietary regimen was best for her and how to attain it.

But *how* did Stella track her diet so precisely? Caley knew the complexities of combining many foods into a balanced diet—even professional dietitians have to use computer programs to manage this. Could it be, she might have been forgiven for wondering, that Stella was secretly an expert in nutrition? Except that Stella was a baboon.

A confounding story, when you consider all the dietary advice we humans seem to require in order to eat properly (not that it does most of us a lot of good).

Meanwhile, our wild cousin, the baboon, apparently has figured it all out by instinct. How could such a thing be so?

Before we begin to explore that question, here's another tale, even weirder. It starts with a lab scientist named Audrey Dussutour at the University of Sydney. One day Audrey took her scalpel and started preparing an experiment by cutting a gooey blob of slime mold into small pieces. Beside her on the bench sat hundreds of Petri dishes, all set out neatly in rows.

Audrey picked up each fragment of yellow goo with forceps and carefully transferred it into the center of a dish, then covered it with a lid. The dishes contained either small blocks of protein or carbohydrate, or a wheel of eleven tiny bits of jelly-like food medium varying in the ratio of protein to carbs. Once all dishes had received their bit of slime mold, Audrey stacked them in a large cardboard box and left them overnight.

The next day, she opened the box and laid out the dishes again on the bench. When she looked closely, she was astonished. Each bit of goo had changed overnight. When the slime molds were offered two blocks of food—one of protein, the other of carbs—the blobs extended their growing tendrils to *both* nutrients, reaching out just far enough in each direction to pull in a mix of the two. That mixture contained precisely two parts protein to one part carbs. Even more incredibly, when bits of goo were placed in dishes containing eleven different food blocks, the tendrils grew overnight from the center of the dish to colonize only the blocks containing that same two-to-one nutrient mixture, ignoring the rest.

What is so special about a diet of two parts protein to one part carbs? The answer came when Audrey placed pieces of slime mold into dishes containing differing combinations of protein and carbohydrate. The next day, some bits of slime remained stunted, whereas others had grown dramatically, extending themselves across the dish in a lacy network of pulsing yellow filaments. When Audrey later mapped the growth of the blobs, it was as if she had charted the up-and-down contours of a mountain. Goo placed on a nutrient that was two parts protein to one part carbs sat at the summit of the growth mountain. As the proportion of protein fell and carbs rose, or vice versa, the blobs' growth decreased. In other words, when the bits of slime mold were given the chance to select their own diet, they chose precisely the mixture of nutrients needed to optimize healthy development.

Audrey's yellow goo with the remarkable nutritional wisdom is a creature with the scientific name *Physarum polycephalum*—literally, many-headed slime. It is the real-life version of *The Blob* of B-movie fame. It is seldom seen, but like other slime molds (including the wonderfully named dog's-vomit slime mold) and fungi, it lives a secretive life among the leaf litter, logs, and soils of the world's forest floors. It is a single-celled creature with millions of nuclei, which can regenerate itself from tiny pieces, crawl like a giant amoeba, and grow its own complex, reticulated architecture of tubes that pulse and distribute nutrients around its network. It simply creates tentacles and then reaches out with them to grab whatever it wants to eat. Fascinating, if a little horrifying.

Now, we may be able to accept that Stella the baboon can make some wise nutritional decisions. But how can a single-celled creature without organs or limbs, let alone a brain or a centralized nervous system, make such sophisticated dietary choices and then carry them out?

This puzzled us, too, so, we asked an expert.

Professor John Tyler-Bonner passed Steve a laboratory beaker filled with steaming coffee, freshly brewed on the naked blue Bunsen burner flame that hissed quietly on the teak benchtop. Steve sat discussing Audrey's results with this venerable guru of slime mold biology in John's office—a time capsule that has not been refurbished since 1947, when John first arrived on faculty at the Department of Ecology and Evolutionary Biology at Princeton University. He pioneered the study of slime molds, and his work has helped lay the foundation for the study of complex decision-making within distributed entities, such as bird flocks and fish schools, crowds of people, or global corporations.

John explained that each part of the blob senses its local nutritional environment and responds accordingly. As a result, the entire blob acts as if it is a single sentient being, seeking out optimal sources of food—a balanced diet that will ensure favorable health—and rejecting what does not serve that goal.

This, you may agree, is better than what is achieved by some other sentient beings we could name. And this, as you probably realize by now, has everything to do with the subject at hand.

Why have we, two entomologists, written a book about human diet, nutrition, and health, a subject on which quite a few experts have already weighed in (no pun intended)? We didn't start out meaning to do any such thing. Throughout our lives as scientists, and especially during the first two decades of our thirty-two-year collaboration, we have studied insects in an attempt to solve one of nature's most enduring riddles: How do living things know what to eat?

Answer that and you've learned something very important—possibly even useful—about life itself. And not just for insects. But we're getting ahead of ourselves now. Better to start at the beginning.

1

The Day of the Locusts

THE YEAR IS 1991. WE ARE SITTING TOGETHER AT Steve's computer in his office in the Oxford University Museum of Natural History—the same place that in 1860 hosted the "great debate" over Darwinian evolution between Thomas Henry Huxley and the Bishop of Oxford, Samuel Wilberforce. That legendary encounter is best remembered for a heated exchange in which Wilberforce supposedly asked Huxley, who was known as Darwin's "bulldog," which of his grandparents was descended from monkeys. Huxley is said to have replied that he would not mind having a monkey as his ancestor, but he would be ashamed to be related to someone who used his great gifts to obscure the truth.

We had just performed the biggest dietary experiments we'd ever attempted. The study involved locusts, which are a special type of grasshopper and, as we will explain below, the ideal animal for our study.

Little did we know that before our session that day was over, the seeds for a new approach to nutrition, one heavily dependent on Darwin's theory, would be sown.

We wanted to answer two questions. First, do animals decide what to eat based on what's best for them? And second, what happens if for some reason they fail to follow that diet and eat another one instead?

You can see how these answers might be somewhat important.

Twenty-five foods had been carefully prepared in the lab to differ in the balance of protein to carbs, the two main nutrients consumed by herbivorous insects such as locusts. The foods ranged from high protein/low carb (a bit like meat) to high carb/low protein (more like rice) and everything in between.

Despite their varying compositions, the foods all looked very similar: they were dry and granular, a bit like cake mix before adding the liquid. The insects seemed to like them.

The mixtures were fed to the locusts, each of which could eat as much as it liked, but only of the single food it was given, until it molted to become an adult. This took a minimum of nine days and up to three weeks, depending on the food. Logistically, then, quite a challenge—painstakingly preparing twenty-five different foods, feeding one to each of two hundred insects, and then meticulously measuring how much every individual had consumed each day.

During the experiment, we spent what felt like endless hours together deep in the bowels of the Zoology Department in a cramped, humid room heated to 90 degrees Fahrenheit—a temperature at which desert-living locusts thrive but which can test a human friendship. Music helped—John Cale and Talking Heads kept us sane. Each locust lived within its own plastic box, with a metal perch to rest upon, a small dish of its assigned food that had been weighed to the nearest tenth of a milligram, and a water dish.

Every day we had to remove each locust's food dish and, like meticulous sewerage workers, pick out any pellets of locust poo from the food dish and box. We measured how much was eaten and digested by weighing food dishes before and after feeding and analyzing excrement. Every food dish had to be placed in a desiccator to dry off any moisture and was then reweighed on a set of electronic scales that could detect a change of one hundred thousandths of a gram. By measuring the difference in weight of the food dish before and after feeding, we calculated how much the insect had eaten that day, and from that we could determine exactly how much protein and carbs it had consumed.

We did this for all two hundred locusts day after day until they either successfully molted to become winged adults or died beforehand. We recorded how many days that took, measured the animal's weight, and analyzed how much fat and lean tissue they had grown.

And then, at last, we were side by side at Steve's computer, about to learn the results of the experiment. In order to understand the results, we should first take a look at locusts in their natural context. After all, they didn't evolve while living in a basement lab at Oxford. And, as we show throughout this book, nothing about nutrition makes sense unless you understand the biological context in which the species evolved, ours included.

Two juvenile locusts, somewhere in North Africa.

One grew up on her own. It hasn't rained locally for months, and other locusts are few and far between. She is a beautiful shade of green, which allows her to blend in with the vegetation. She has a solitary existence, being shy in her behavior and repelled by other locusts. For good reason: one locust can hide; larger groups will attract unwanted attention from hungry birds, lizards, and hunting spiders.

Elsewhere, another locust was reared in a crowd. It rained not so long ago, and others like her are around in large numbers, feasting on the abundant vegetation. She is a party animal—brightly colored, very active, and attracted into groups. These aggregations form marching bands, and when they become winged adults, flying swarms that migrate across vast areas of Africa and Asia. A plague of the desert locust in North Africa can contain hundreds of billions of insects and eat as much in a single day as the entire population of New York will in a week. When they move into agricultural areas, they are devastating (locusts, not New Yorkers).

The two locusts are not different species (as was thought originally)—they could even be sisters. Every one of their kind has the potential to become either a shy green grasshopper or a gregarious extrovert, depending on whether they grow up alone or in a crowd. The process of changing from one form to the other occurs quickly. If you took the solitary green grasshopper and put her in a crowd, within an hour she would be attracted rather than repelled by other locusts, and a few hours later she could be part of a marching band. Before long she will change from green to being brightly colored.

This transition is known as *density dependent behavioral phase change*, and Steve's research group spent years trying to understand it.

One of the initial questions we had was this: What is it about being in a crowd that causes the change? What stimuli are provided by other locusts that might trigger the transition? Could it be the sight of them, their smell, their sound?

As we discovered, touch is what's critical. When there is a limited availability of suitable food plants, solitary locusts are forced to forage nearer each other than they'd prefer. The congregated insects jostle one another, and this physical contact causes the change from repulsion to attraction.

Once enough gregarious locusts come together, suddenly, as if of one mind, the entire group becomes highly aligned and starts to march.

We found that the collective decision to start marching emerges within a crowd from simple local interactions among locusts. In other words, there is no leader locust or hierarchical control. Marching emerges because the locusts are all following one easy rule: "align with your moving neighbors." Once a critical density of locusts is reached, just adding one or two more will suddenly cause the transition to collective, aligned movement. The terrible march has begun.

Of course, we still didn't understand *why* locusts should follow the simple rule to align with their moving neighbors. We suspected that nutrition may play a role—as it does in most things. The answer came from our study of a related animal called the Mormon cricket, and it turned out that their motive was rather sinister.

The Mormon cricket is a large, flightless insect built like a small tank that lives in the southwestern United States and forms vast marching swarms extending miles. They are called this because they began to devastate the first crops planted by the Mormon pioneers after arriving at Salt Lake in 1848. The community was powerless to stop the destruction and were facing starvation until, in the nick of time, a flock of seagulls came to the rescue and ate the crickets. There is now a monument to the gulls commemorating this event at the Temple in Salt Lake City. The seagull is the state bird of Utah (an odd thing, considering that it's landlocked, but gulls find their way to any large body of water).

Steve was in Utah, studying swarms of Mormon crickets with colleagues Greg Sword, Pat Lorch, and Iain Couzin, when they discovered the reason behind its sudden decision to align and begin marching. As Steve explains:

We were staying in a truck stop motel, eating junk food washed down with Polygamy Porter (slogan: "Why have just one?"). The crickets were about in huge numbers. Greg and Pat had radio-tracked vast bands moving up to two kilometers each day through the spectacular sagebrush country.

Here's a clue to why all those crickets were migrating. We recorded a single band of them crossing a main road for five continuous days. When they got squashed by cars, those following behind stopped to eat the corpses. And got squashed by cars. Before long, the mess was ankle deep, and snowplows had to be dispatched to clear the greasy slurry.

But why might herbivorous insects so avidly eat one another, even to the point of mass suicide? After all, with lots of vegetation around, there were plenty of other things for them to consume.

We had brought along to the desert the same dry, powdery feeds used in our big locust study back at Oxford, and we laid dishes of it out in front of the marching cricket bands.

The result was revealing. The crickets ignored the dishes of high-carb food but stopped to eat from the ones containing protein.

And aside from our little buffet, what was the nearest source of high-quality protein to those crickets? The cricket in front. What was forcing the march was simple: if you don't move forward when your neighbors to the rear do, they will eat you. Meanwhile, of course, if the creature in front of you stops, you may seize upon it as a meal. Cricket cannibalism was driven by a powerful appetite—for protein.

And we discovered that locust habits can be equally gruesome when it comes to hungering for that nutrient. We learned this inadvertently, when Steve was trying to explore the signals that tell locusts when they are full during a meal. In an experiment, he had laboriously cut the nerves carrying feeling from the end of the insects' abdomens to their brains. After the surgery, he put all the locusts in the same box to recover. Next morning, when Steve looked, he saw that none of the locusts had a body left below the point where the nerve had been cut. The insects had formed a kind of daisy chain, chewing off the hind end of the locust in front (who couldn't feel a thing) while at the same time having its own numbed abdomen eaten by the locust behind.

What better animal, then, to use for testing big ideas in nutrition science? If any species would be expected to be gluttonous and eat as much as possible of whatever the food provided, then voracious swarming locusts are it. But we knew that locusts are not so simple-minded—they can regulate their intake of nutrients, notably protein, even if that requires consuming their neighbors. What would the results of our big experiment show?

Before we find out, we first need to provide a short primer on nutrition.

CHAPTER 1 AT A GLANCE

1. We began our journey by describing an experiment on locusts, which pioneered a new approach to the study of nutrition.
2. We discovered that an appetite for protein is behind locusts' reputation as plague-forming scourges of agriculture.
3. Will an appetite for protein play similarly important roles elsewhere in the animal kingdom? Even for us?

2

Calories and Nutrients

GIVEN THAT NUTRITION IS SO INFERNALLY COMplicated, let's ask a simple question: Why must we eat?

Certainly, food today has become the source of a great deal of confusion and anxiety, which is a terrible pity because food is also the source of so much that is good—excellent, in fact. Food binds us together socially and culturally. It gives a great deal of pleasure while also providing the stuff that fuels life itself.

Energy is the most familiar of the things we need from food. Not a day goes by without seeing numbers written all over our foods, meals, and now also menus—like mathematical graffiti saying how much energy they contain and stern dietary guidelines warning how much of it we should eat. The labels don't use the word *energy*, of course. You're probably more familiar with the term *Calories*.

But what exactly *is* a Calorie?

It's simply a unit of energy—a single Calorie is the amount of energy needed to raise the temperature of 1 kilogram (2.2 pounds) of water (which is the same as a liter) by 1 degree Celsius, from 14.5 to 15.5 C. Yes, this is a bizarre currency indeed, except, perhaps, if you have ever wondered how much food it takes to heat a bathtub. But it is rigorously exact, which we scientists tend to like. And so, everyone is stuck thinking in calories, even though they are hard to picture.

To confuse things further, you may also see calories written as kilocalories (kcal). This is because 1 Calorie (with a big "C") equals 1,000 calories (with a small "c"). You may also have seen the energy content of a food presented as kJ—kilojoules, which is what we scientists mainly use, along with kcal. These units have an even more unlikely-sounding definition: 1 kJ is the energy needed to move a 1-kilogram (2.2-pound) weight by a force of 1 Newton (which is itself a measure of gravitational pull), over a distance of 1 meter. One kilojoule equals 0.239006 Calorie (to be exact!).

In this book we will mainly use "kcal" when presenting units of energy, but on occasions when presenting scientific results, we will use "kJ." Throughout, we will use "calories" with a small "c" as a generic term for "energy."

This means we determine the energy contained in food based on its theoretical power to fuel action—to heat water or move weights.

All food contains calories, with the exception of water, which is just as well, because without energy, our bodies wouldn't be able to do anything, including make use of the other important thing we take from food: nutrients. Energy comes from the main nutrients in our diet—the macronutrients, as they are known—each of which is chemically different. Once we consume these nutritional fuels—proteins, carbohydrates, and fats—they are broken down into smaller molecules that are burned within our cells.

Macronutrients deliver more than just energy, however. Proteins and their building blocks, the amino acids, also supply nitrogen, with which we make all sorts of other important things, including hormones, enzymes, and the information-storing molecules DNA and RNA. If we don't ingest protein, we don't live.

In the popular mind (and in many diet books), fats and carbohydrates (carbs) have almost become just another way of saying "Calories," but there is a lot more to them than that. Fats insulate us from the cold, store vitamins, lubricate the skin, and cushion our eyeballs and joints. Their fatty acid building blocks make up the membrane that surrounds every cell in our bodies, and special fats called *sterols* serve as messengers that help coordinate the complex chemistry that keeps us alive.

We can't do without fats.

Carbohydrates include sugars, starches, and fibers. Like proteins and fats, most carbs are built of smaller units, in this case, simple sugars such as glucose and fructose. The nutritional properties of different carbs depend on which simple sugars they consist of and how they are strung together. The most abundant carbohydrate on our planet—the plant fiber cellulose—has its glucose units strung together so tightly that we can't digest it.

Glucose is particularly important because it's the main carbohydrate on which our bodies depend. In addition to providing energy, glucose partners with the nitrogen from protein in the synthesis of DNA and RNA.

Our bodies can create glucose by breaking down proteins and fats, so, strictly speaking, we don't have to eat *any* carbs to get glucose. But that is not the same thing as saying we don't need to eat carbs at all—as we will show later.

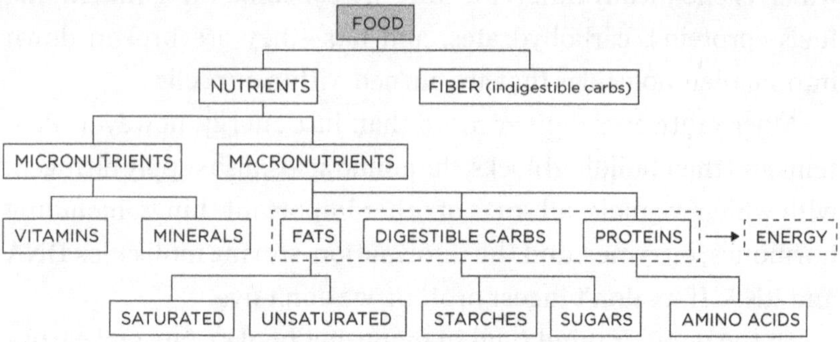

A schematic showing the relationship between foods, nutrients, and energy.

And those are just the macronutrients. Vitamins and minerals are needed, too, though in tiny amounts compared with the big three, which is why they are called *micronutrients.* These are used by the body for too many purposes to mention here. But keep in mind that sodium, calcium, magnesium, chloride, and potassium all generate electrical currents that quite literally make us tick—our hearts beat and our nerve cells crackle with electrical impulses.

The diagram above provides a summary of what's in food. Should you want to know more about the different boxes in the diagram, check out More on Nutrients on pages 203–213, which may also be of use at specific points when reading the rest of the book.

As we can see from the diagram, foods are complex mixtures of many nutrients; not to mention diets, which are themselves complex mixtures of foods. To understand nutrition, we need to think not in terms of single nutrients but rather the *balance* of nutrients in these mixtures.

If an animal is to thrive, it needs to eat macro- and micronutrients in the right amounts—like Goldilocks, not too little, not too much. Some animals, such as parasites living within the body of their host, get all the nutrients they need, and in the right balance, from a single food source. For them, choosing the proper diet is easy. All mammals, including ourselves, are lucky to start life in such ideal circumstances—because mother's milk is as close as we'll ever come to a perfectly balanced diet. It contains, in proper proportions, everything a newborn needs to grow. But after a mammal is weaned, nutrition becomes a much trickier undertaking.

It's easy to see why. The things we eat are made up of nutrients in almost endless combinations. Some foods are richer in protein, others in fats or carbs—but all are mixtures. There *are* no single-nutrient foods. Pasta and bread certainly live up to their carb-rich reputations, but about 10 percent of the energy they contain comes from protein. A steak is a protein powerhouse but more than half of it is water, along with lots of fat and minerals, too.

We humans complicate matters even further because, unlike other animals, we tend not to eat single foods; rather, we assemble them into recipes and meals. Then we combine meals into varied diets and dietary patterns, sending complex mixtures of nutrients and other substances into our bodies, where they interact with our physiology.

Now, imagine having to consciously navigate and balance the proper mixture of all that on a thrice-daily basis. We would all need PhDs in mathematics and computing, and even then the calculations wouldn't leave us time to do much else.

Thankfully, as Stella the baboon and the slimy blob showed us, nature is capable of handling complex challenges like this one without mathematics and computers. The solution is simple and elegant—and exists inside every living thing, as we shall see before long. But first, back to Oxford.

CHAPTER 2 AT A GLANCE

1. The key players in nutrition are calories, macronutrients (protein, carbs, and fat), micronutrients, and fiber.
2. You can check out More on Nutrients on pages 203–213 for extra detail.
3. Nutrition is about more than single things (fat, sugar, protein, or whatever)—it's about *mixtures* of dietary nutrients and about their *balance*.
4. Mixing a nutritionally balanced diet seems daunting, but animals in the wild do it instinctively. How do they do it—and why is it so hard for us?

3

Picturing Nutrition

WITH CALORIES AND NUTRIENTS IN MIND, LET'S return to Oxford, where we left off in Chapter 1 sitting side by side at Steve's computer to view the results of our big locust experiment. As was (and still is) usual for us, the first step was to make a simple visual representation of the data—a graph.

The graph itself looked like a large letter L. The vertical line, or axis, is where the computer would mark how much carbohydrate an insect ate in milligrams (mg). The horizontal axis would show how many milligrams of protein that locust consumed. Before we show the actual results, to help explain how to read the graph, here's the hypothetical example of a locust that ate 300 mg of carbs and 200 mg of protein:

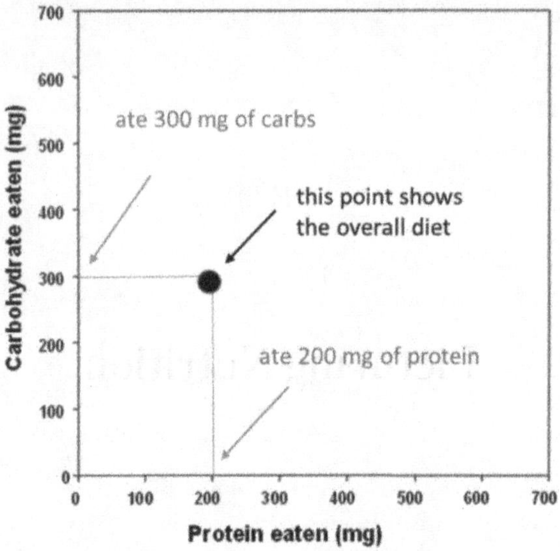

A graph showing how the intake of a locust eating 300 mg carbs and 200 mg protein would be plotted.

When we plotted the actual results for all the locusts across all the diets, we saw something fascinating. The intake points fell neatly along a line, rising like a drifting plume from the horizontal axis. So astoundingly simple was the pattern, that at first we suspected there was a problem with our arithmetic. We checked it and double-checked it. All was right.

Then we realized what we were seeing was real and important—although at the time, we didn't know just *how* important. We were seeing, for the first time, how appetites for different nutrients interact to deal with nutritional imbalance. And, we already knew, dealing with nutritional imbalance is a big deal, a very big deal, in the natural lives of animals—it is essential for success. More than that, we had invented a new approach, which can be applied to *any* species, for unravelling the mysteries of eating. We called this Nutritional Geometry.

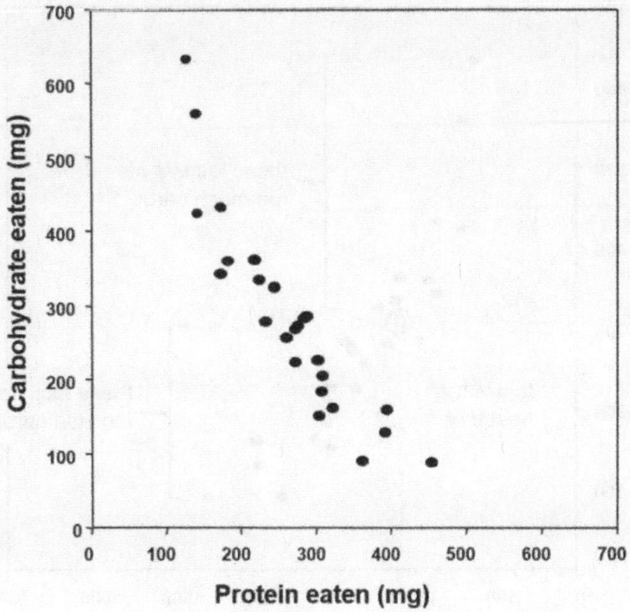

The plot of results from the locust experiment. Each point shows the protein and carbohydrate intakes (as illustrated in the previous plot) of locusts fed one particular diet. Note how the points rise upward in a plume. Each point shows the average intake of one group of locusts.

Having graphed the results, the next step was to work out which of the diets was closest to being nutritionally balanced for a locust. For that, we identified the mixture of protein and carbs that allowed locusts to grow and survive best—essentially, the healthiest nutrient balance possible. We called this the *target diet* and have marked it on the next graph with a bull's-eye.

As you might imagine, the target is rather important not just for the locusts but for the concept of Nutritional Geometry itself. It allows us to see, at a glance, which diets are best balanced (the black points near the bull's-eye) and which are imbalanced—all the rest. The further from the target, the more imbalanced. We can also see how exactly a diet is imbalanced. Those points above

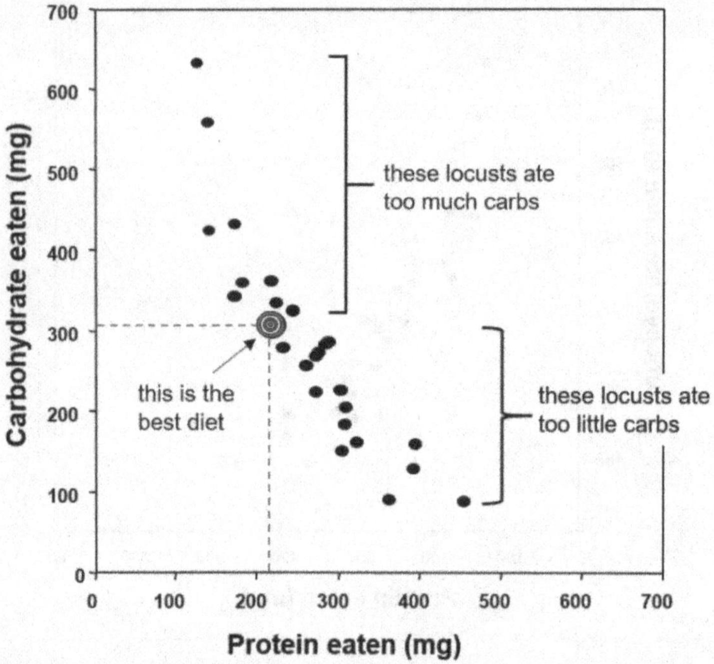

The bull's-eye shows the diet that supported best survival and growth. Other points can then be interpreted relative to this target diet.

the target show locusts that ate too much carbs; those below ate too little. Only those on the target ate exactly the right amount!

With those simple concepts in place, you can see something else that is important in our results. The locusts that ate too much carbs all line up vertically close to in line with the protein target, getting a similar amount of protein (about 150 mg, which is approaching the target of 210 mg). But to do so, they have had to overeat carbs—by a lot. And eating those extra carbs came at a cost—well, two costs. First, it took time. It meant that locusts on the low-protein, high-carb diets had to extend the period until they molted to become winged adults. The longer a locust delays getting to adulthood, the more likely it is to be eaten by a bird, lizard, spider—or another locust—before getting a chance to reproduce. The second price they paid is something you wouldn't readily associate with an insect: locusts on the high-carb diets became obese. Granted, it's hard to tell that a locust is fat, because its skeleton is on the outside. But it's chubby on the inside, like an overweight knight wedged into a suit of armor a few sizes too small.

Locusts overate on high-carb diets to reach the protein intake target. But what about low-carb diets? Here we need to focus on the locusts below the bull's-eye in the graph. You can see that the pattern of dots bulges out a bit to the right, meaning that the locusts' protein intake was a bit higher than their target but way down on carbs. As a result, they were too lean and less likely to survive to adulthood compared with locusts on the target diet. Their body fat stores were so low that they would have been unable to fly far or live for long in the wild.

Once again: on high-carb feed, the insects had to keep eating (in order to get all the protein their bodies demanded), and they ended up consuming more carbohydrate than needed, becoming fat, and having to delay development. On low-carb food, they took in less carbohydrate (because they got their fill of protein sooner) but paid the price of being short of energy.

Our locust experiment had documented for the first time in any animal the battle between two nutrients—protein and carbs—as they competed for control of food intake on imbalanced diets. Protein won in the end. In fact, what we were seeing was not so much a competition between two nutrients but between two *appetites*—one for protein, the other for carbs. We next wondered whether the two appetites could work together to help the animal achieve its nutrition goal—a balanced diet.

CHAPTER 3 AT A GLANCE

1. The Oxford locust experiment provided a new way to define balanced and imbalanced diets.
2. Locusts had a target mix of protein and carbs for best growth and survival.
3. When their diet didn't allow them to reach the target, protein was prioritized over carbs but at a cost to growth and survival.
4. We had documented for the first time the battle between two appetites—for protein and carbs. Can these two appetites work together to help the animal achieve its nutrition goal—a balanced diet?

4

Dance of the Appetites

IN THE EXPERIMENT, OUR LOCUSTS WERE EACH given a single food to eat. They could eat as much of it as they wanted, but they *couldn't* change the balance of protein and carbs—that was determined by us. We had done this to set up a competition between the two appetites for protein and carbs to see which was more powerful; and as we just saw, protein won.

But what would have happened had the locusts been free to choose from a variety of foods? Would their appetites have worked together to help the insects navigate the proper balance of protein and carbs?

We asked a PhD student in our lab at Oxford, Paul Chambers, to create a nutritional challenge for locusts to solve. He offered the insects choices of two foods differing in their protein and carb content.

In every case, the insects did the exact same thing: they ate an identical balance of protein and carbs, regardless of which foods they were offered. To do so, they had to choose very different amounts of the two foods, depending on which pair was offered. It's as if, regardless of whether we were offered meat and pasta, or egg and bread, or beans and rice, or fish and potatoes, we always consumed the exact same balance of protein and carbs. For us humans, this might seem a nearly impossible challenge. Somehow, the locusts solved the puzzle with ease.

Even more impressive, the combination of protein and carbs they chose exactly matched the bull's-eye in our graph from the big locust experiment. They had chosen the healthiest combination of protein and carbs, the one that best supported survival and growth.

Our experiments even showed *how* the insects could tell if a food contained the nutrient they lacked. Locusts, like other insects, have taste hairs all over their mouthparts as well as on their feet and elsewhere. When these hairs touch something edible, the locust analyzes its chemical content before deciding whether to eat. If, say, the insect has recently taken in enough protein, these sensors will ignore that nutrient. It won't even recognize that the nutrient is there. If, on the other hand, the locust is protein-deficient, the sensors, upon encountering protein, will send electrical messages to the brain saying, "Eat this"—and that is exactly what ours did, ignoring carbs.

We went one step further and showed that locusts could even learn to associate colors and scents with the protein and carb content of foods. We could train them to go to places where they had come to learn they would find what they craved. That's a pretty smart thing to do for an animal with a brain the size of a pin head.

This proved that when locusts have a good choice of available foods, their appetite systems collaborate, and the insects combine the foods in exactly the right proportions to consume an optimally balanced diet. But when they are restricted to imbalanced foods, as in our big locust experiment, the appetites for protein and carbohydrate compete. And for locusts, in the end, protein always won.

All this detail about locust feeding was fascinating in itself—for us, at least. But it also raised a much bigger issue relevant to everybody: the possibility that what we had seen in locusts might apply to appetites across the entire animal kingdom, including humans. It is therefore worth looking at exactly what appetites are and how they work their magic (and sometimes, their mischief). This line of inquiry will also help answer a question that we are often asked: *How do living things know, innately, what they ought to eat?*

The first thing to bear in mind when trying to understand appetite is that nature has provided everything we eat with highly individual tastes—flavors. To us, a hunk of charred flesh tastes different from a handful of berries, which is different again from a bunch of juicy, dark green leaves. All this variety is no accident, nor is it simply to keep us from being bored at mealtime (but it does that, too). The flavor profile of a food indicates its chemical contents—its nutrients.

Given that proteins, fats, and carbs each have their own special roles and significance, both to provide energy and to perform other important functions, it comes as no surprise that nature has equipped us with the ability to tell the difference and thereby detect their presence in food.

We take this talent for granted, but without it, none of us would exist. It helps us to know what nutrients are contained in which foods and what we should eat and avoid. This need to find the proper foods is why we experience sugar as tasting pleasingly sweet, and why high-protein foods have that lip-smacking savory taste that the Japanese call *umami*, and fats have that rich, buttery mouth feel and flavor. Otherwise, how would we tell the nutrients apart?

We are not alone among the animal kingdom in being able to taste macronutrients, although some other animals possess their taste organs in unlikely places. A female blowfly, like a locust, tastes sugar and amino acids with her feet and with the tip of her abdomen to guide laying eggs on something suitably disgusting (to us at least) for growing her baby maggots. If that sounds gross, consider that we have taste receptors inside our intestines as well as in our mouths to help keep track of nutrients as they are broken down during digestion. After all, our gut is open at both ends—just as we taste food at the front end, we keep track of it all the way through. We even continue to detect nutrients after they leave the gut and enter the bloodstream, using receptors located in various organs—including the liver and the brain. The brain is where the appetite control centers reside. These are the neural circuits that collect together signals from the bloodstream, liver, and gut, generating feelings of hunger and fullness.

As is true for macronutrients, we have taste organs that can detect some of the micronutrients, including mineral salts, both on our tongues and scattered through our bodies.

Specific tastes and flavors provide information about which foods are which and how much of particular nutrients each contains. They are the external side of the feeding equation. This helps an animal decide *what* to eat, and there's no need for us to tell you the importance of that. But tastes and flavors are not much good at telling the animal something equally important: how much of each nutrient it needs at a given time. That, the internal half of the equation, is taken care of by appetite systems.

It is a mistake, and one that is much more common than it ought to be, to think of appetite as a single, powerful hunger that drives animals (including us) to eat until they are full. As our locusts taught us, a single appetite would be useless for mixing a balanced diet. Therefore, animals need *separate* appetites to keep track of the different nutrients they need.

And yet, there is a limit to how complex biological systems can get and still operate efficiently. For this reason, we couldn't possibly have specific appetites for each and every one of the dozens of nutrients needed to keep us alive and well. It would probably drive us mad at mealtime.

Instead, we found two appetites in locusts—one for protein and the other for carbs. What about more complex species, like humans? How many appetites do *we* need? Perhaps a better way to ask this is how *few* nutrient-specific appetites does it take to keep us alive and well?

The answer, it seems, is five. Five appetites are sufficient. They drive us to consume the following nutrients:

Protein
Carbs
Fats
Sodium
Calcium

These are the three macronutrients plus two critically important micronutrients. These correspond precisely to the same nutrients that we are able to taste in foods. A most elegant solution to an otherwise impossible challenge. Our appetites have evolved to target specific flavors and guide us to eat only the things we need to survive.

Those nutrients (the Big Five) have been singled out by our evolution for special reasons. One is that they are needed in the diet at very specific levels—neither too much nor too little. Another is that the things we eat vary widely in their concentrations of these nutrients—we would, for example, need to eat a lot more rice than steak to get the amount of protein we require. Third, some of these nutrients were so rare in our ancestral environments that we needed dedicated biological machinery to seek them out.

For example, sodium and calcium were once so scarce that they were assigned dedicated appetites with their own specific taste receptors—and we are not alone in this. We get the word *salary* because salt was so prized, it was used in historical times as a monetary currency. Gorillas eat tree bark to get enough salt. Calcium is so prized by giant pandas that it causes them to migrate long distances to get enough to breed.

What about the other essential nutrients—such as vitamins A, C, D, E, K, B_1 (thiamine), B_2 (riboflavin), B_3 (niacin), B_5 (pantothenic acid), B_6, B_7 (biotin), B_9 (folate), or B_{12}, or minerals like potassium, chlorine, phosphorus, magnesium, iron, zinc, manganese, copper, iodine, chromium, molybdenum, selenium, and cobalt? Why didn't we evolve specific appetites for them? One reason is that our natural diets are rich in these nutrients, and by eating the right amounts of the Big Five, we automatically get enough of the rest. That's a lot of measurements and calculations we've been spared.

If all of the above sounds pretty logical, that's because it is. But it hasn't always been viewed that way, even by the experts.

For over six hundred years, the word *appetite* was used in much the same way, both in everyday conversation and by experts. As long ago as 1375, the Scotsman John Barbour wrote in a poem of a hearty feast that needed "no other sauce—except appetite"; the same idea has become immortalized in the idiom "hunger is the best sauce." A few years later, in 1398, Chaucer observed that the strength of the appetite is dependent on good health: "Weak appetite cometh before sickness"; and in 1789, Benjamin Franklin made the link between appetite and our nutrient needs: "What one relishes, nourishes."

The scientific study of appetite is more recent. It all started with an important question: Exactly what is it in our bodies that makes us feel hungry? An early theory, which dates to 1912, was what has come to be known as the *rumble theory*. According to this, stomach fullness is the switch for appetite: hunger is turned on when the walls of an empty, churning stomach rub against each other ("rumble") and turned off when it is full. The rumble theory took a fatal blow when it was later found that a stomach was not needed to feel hungry: patients who had had their stomachs surgically removed to treat cancer or ulcers continued to experience those familiar pangs.

Several theories followed, each one proposing a different measurement made by the body to tell our brains when we should eat. The *thermostatic hypothesis* suggested that animals ate to get enough energy to keep warm and stopped eating to prevent overheating; the *glucostatic hypothesis* identified blood sugar as the important link; the *lipostatic theory* implicated body fat reserves; and the *aminostatic theory* argued that amino acids circulating in the blood were responsible. While obviously different, all of these theories had in common that they identified a single component of the diet as the link between appetite and what the body needed: energy, sugars, fats, or amino acids.

In the 1930s, working quietly and inconspicuously with rats in his lab at Johns Hopkins University, was a young scientist named Curt Richter. The son of a German engineer, Richter had less time for theories than for performing clever experiments to measure exactly how the body instructs the brain to perform specific behaviors, and eating was no exception. Over a period of seventy years, working in the same laboratory, Richter made many discoveries that form an important backdrop to our research and the story in this book.

In one experiment, Richter operated on rats to trick their physiology into losing salt from the body at a fatal rate. And yet they didn't die but rather just ate more salt to compensate for the increased losses. Importantly, they didn't eat more food overall or more of other nutrients, only salt. He did similar experiments for calcium with the same result: the rats saved their own lives by eating more calcium but no more of other nutrients.

To ensure that what he was seeing was relevant to the normal lives of rats, Richter also studied their pattern of food selection in times when female rats naturally had an increased need for sodium and calcium, during pregnancy and lactation. As he suspected, here, too, they selected diets that were higher than usual in these nutrients. Richter's experiments had shown that rats have not one appetite but at least two for different nutrients. All those other theories—thermostatic, glucostatic, lipostatic, and aminostatic—needed a rethink. Not because they were all wrong, but perhaps there were elements of truth in each.

This is where our own research on locusts entered the story. We proved that even in insects there are multiple appetites and that these can be used to select a balanced diet.

But appetites don't exist only to tell us to start eating. Equally important, they also tell us when to stop. This involves nutrients in the food being released by digestion, getting absorbed into the bloodstream, and sending signals of fullness back to the brain. The only flaw is that these signals take time to kick in (in fact, some don't act until after the end of a meal). The risk is that you will have overeaten by the time you get the message to stop. We all know the sensation of eating so much, so quickly, that we didn't realize we were full ten minutes ago. In the meantime, we have delivered a calorie bomb to our system.

How can this be avoided? We need something to slow down our eating, fill us up quickly, and allow time for the slowly absorbed nutrients to reach our blood and announce to the brain that they are there. Luckily, nature has provided us that, too, in the form of a gut-stretcher that induces the feeling of fullness and slows the rate of gut emptying.

Fiber.

For herbivores like locusts and omnivores like us, fiber is the major source of bulk in plant foods. It forms the structure of plant cells and tissues and, as we explained in Chapter 2 and More on Nutrients (page 203), much of it is based on complex forms of carbohydrate that we are unable to digest using our own digestive enzymes. Some of that fiber, however, is digested by microbes that live in our guts—our *microbiome*, as those trillions of bacteria are known collectively.

In return, these microbes produce key nutrients (short-chain fatty acids, vitamins, and amino acids) that our bodies need. They also support our immune systems, keeping our intestines healthy, and even benefit our mental health. In addition to all that, gut microbes produce signals that make us feel full. They are an important part of our appetite control system.

Thanks to locusts and some geometry, we had glimpsed the beauty and power of nutrient appetites. We had seen how they worked together in perfect rhythm when possible—when the correct range of foods was available—to help animals solve the complex challenges of eating a balanced diet. We had also seen, in the locust experiment, that when things got rough and it wasn't possible to eat a balanced diet, the appetites came into conflict. In that case, for locusts, the protein appetite took the lead, and carbs followed more passively.

We began to wonder whether locusts were just an elegant oddity that was not generalizable to the rest of the animal kingdom—let alone to humans. Or were we looking at something like a general rule of nature? If so, that could be important.

CHAPTER 4 AT A GLANCE

1. Animals have evolved separate appetites for protein, carbs, fat, sodium, and calcium. Together, the Big Five can signal a nutritionally balanced diet.
2. Fiber acts as a brake on appetite, preventing overeating and feeding the gut microbiome.
3. When offered an appropriate choice of foods, the protein and carbohydrate appetites work in harmony to guide locusts to consume a balanced diet.
4. But is nutrient balancing universal among all animals?

5

Seeking Exceptions to the Rule

WHEN SCIENTISTS ARE IN PURSUIT OF SOMEthing potentially important, we are trained to temper our enthusiasms and continually ask: *Could we be wrong?* For us, that question took this form: Could it be that the power of multiple appetites to serve an organism's nutritional needs was the exception rather than the rule?

Specifically, in our case, the question was whether the balancing act performed by the feeding locusts in our lab was the rule for other animals, and not just in laboratories but in natural environments. Nutrient balancing using multiple appetites was probably commonplace, we suspected.

This wasn't merely wishful thinking by a pair of scientists wanting to have discovered something important. We had grounds to believe we might be right. In fact, we reasoned that what we were seeing was more or less a *requirement* for all living things.

A compelling reason for our belief comes first from the logic of Darwin. The mechanism by which organisms acquire their various features and skills involves a simple numbers game. Any characteristic that aids successful reproduction, provided it is at least partly heritable, will be passed on to the next generation—more so than characteristics that are unhelpful. Because these traits can be inherited, the offspring whose parents had the useful characteristic will themselves be more successful at reproduction, and in this way the helpful trait will eventually become more common and displace its less helpful equivalents in the population.

In terms of our research, everything we knew about biology was pointing us in the same direction: animals that balance their diets would be better equipped to reproduce than those that did not. For those unfortunate ones, eating would be like a lottery, leaving chance to decide which nutrient needs would be met and which would go hungry. Without appetites to guide the way, animals might get lucky some days and eat the mix of nutrients they need, but most of the time they would fail.

But this merely suggested what was likely, not necessarily what was true. How could we test it? The surest way would be to examine every species on the planet. But with the immense amount of work involved in our locust experiments still fresh in mind, we knew this was never going to happen. We hold the record for the number of different species whose nutritional wisdom has been studied (more than fifty by our reckoning—varying in size from ants to moose), and you will read many of their stories in this book. But that simply scratches the surface.

We needed a different approach.

The most effective way to learn whether nutrient balancing is the rule among animals or is restricted to a few, we realized, would be to reverse the question. We'd test the species that seemed to be *least* likely to balance their nutrient intake. If we were wrong, they'd show us. This kind of self-skepticism, in which theories are tested by seeing how much of a battering they can take and remain standing, is not only usual practice in science but a defining characteristic. This is what makes science *science*.

Anyway, now we needed to seek species that didn't engage in nutrient balancing. If even the unlikeliest candidates were found to do so, we could be confident that most if not all do. Which species were particularly likely to disprove our theory? In a sense, we already had studied one of them. Of all animals, locusts were among the most renowned for an indiscriminate greed, devouring everything in their path. Having shown that even *they* meticulously compiled a precise mix of nutrients in their diet gave us confidence that so, too, would other species, especially those already known to be fussy eaters.

An even stiffer challenge then arose through a chance encounter involving a cacophony of chirping chickens, a student with a philosophical bent, and two halves of bugger-all.

It was 1997, when David was in the Lancaster lab of Oxford Zoology Department teaching a practical course in animal behavior. The students were busy with an experiment involving groups of recently hatched chickens. David was at the front of the class talking to the celebrated evolutionary biologist and devout atheist Richard Dawkins, who had stopped in to see what all the chirping was about.

Seeing his opportunity, an earnest young student named Stephen Jones approached and addressed Richard in a well-spoken English voice: "I am interested in writing an essay on postmodernist science. Would you be prepared to supervise this?"

"What is postmodernist science, in any case?" Richard asked in his characteristic laconic style. Then he immediately answered his own question: "Exactly two halves of bugger-all," a pungent Britishism we can translate as "fuck-all," or, if we're being decorous, absolutely nothing.

Richard well knew—better than most—that "postmodernist science" is a form of cultural relativism, a philosophical view according to which science is just another belief system equivalent to any other, with no monopoly on the truth. This, he knew, was wrong for reasons we discussed above: science's self-skeptical nature is an efficient filter for eliminating incorrect theories and in this way, over time, separating fact from belief.

Richard declined to supervise Stephen's essay. But David, having developed an interest in what was often a fine line that separates "belief" from "fact" in nutrition science, accepted.

Stephen did a fine job. Even though his paper didn't make any game-changing contributions to the philosophy of what is and what is not true, it would indirectly make an important contribution to our search for the truth about feeding.

Through working on the essay, Stephen developed an interest in doing PhD research and wanted to study something of practical importance. He chose to work on cockroaches, those widespread pests with filthy habits, a bad smell, and a reputation for spreading disease. We immediately saw an opportunity: cockroaches were also perfect animals for testing whether nutrient balancing is general to animals.

Here's why. These unlikable creatures are extremely wily, adaptable, and hardy. They can live in virtually all environments from tropical and temperate forests to salt marshes, deserts, and cities, enduring circumstances that would endanger most species. In cities, they are equally at home scavenging in garbage bins, drains, and sewers as in restaurants, pantries, and, given half a chance, your dinner plate, even moving among these venues in a single sitting. Underlying this flexibility is a remarkable capacity to survive on a very wide range of diets, including no diet at all—they can live for a month without eating or drinking and over one hundred days on water alone. A few very special tricks underpin this nutritional hardiness.

Inside the hindguts of cockroaches are thousands of tiny spines. Each houses millions of bacteria, which can digest sources of carbohydrate that to most animals would be useless. Cellulose, for example, the stuff of which wood, paper, cardboard, and cotton fabric are made, can be eaten by cockroaches and used for energy courtesy of their spine-living bacteria. Considering that cellulose is the most abundant organic compound on Earth and few other animals can use it for energy, this is a handy advantage; it means that for cockroaches there is almost never a shortage of carbohydrate.

It doesn't end there. All animals need to get rid of nitrogen wastes that result from various metabolic processes involving protein synthesis and breakdown. In mammals, this is the main function of urine, whereas most insects, birds, and reptiles dump it as a white paste of uric acid. If cockroaches eat too much protein, they, too, excrete the excess as nitrogen wastes. But unlike other animals, they don't excrete it all: some is stored as tiny crystals in specialized cells called *urocytes*, which are found in the insect equivalent of a liver, the fat body. Alongside the urocytes is another kind of fat body cell, called *mycetocytes*. These maintain captive populations of bacteria that are unable to live anywhere else in the world. Their job is to use the nitrogen stored in the urocytes as a raw material to make amino acids, which they release into the blood for use by the cockroach to make protein. Mycetocyte bacteria are, in effect, onboard nitrogen recycling plants.

With such flexible carbohydrate and protein processing abilities, we reasoned, cockroaches would not need to bother nearly as much as other animals about eating the precise levels of sugars, starch, and protein required by their tissues. This, we believed, is why cockroaches can live on such a wide range of diets and why they can survive in so many habitats.

It is also why we were excited at the opportunity to test whether they actually *do* balance their intake of nutrients. If an animal that apparently has no need to eat precisely the right amounts of carbs and protein nonetheless does so, surely then other species that have a greater need would do likewise.

Stephen performed a clever experiment to test this. In a first step, he maintained cockroaches on one of three diets for two days: one group got high protein and low carb, one was fed high carb and low protein, and the third got intermediate levels of both nutrients. In human terms, this would be roughly equivalent to eating either only fish, only rice, or only a mix of fish and rice combined—sushi. After this period, the cockroaches were offered a buffet containing all three diets, from which they could freely select whatever they preferred.

We were surprised by the results. When Stephen plotted the data points in our usual protein-carbohydrate intake graph, we immediately saw that the cockroaches not only balanced their intake of nutrients, but did so with a precision and determination that rivaled anything we'd seen to that point, even to now.

The graph showed that in the final, buffet phase, those cockroaches that had previously been on the sushi-like feed, with balanced levels of protein and carbohydrate, chose from all three foods to compose a diet similar to what they had been eating. The other two groups initially selected *only* the food with the nutrient they were previously denied: if they had been forced to eat only carbs, they now chose protein, and vice versa. They continued eating this way for 10 hours, after which both groups began to eat all three foods. By 48 hours of buffet, they had hit their target nutrient intakes. From that point on, all three groups ate an identical mix of protein and carbohydrate and continued that way until 120 hours later, when the experiment ended.

The message couldn't be clearer. Each insect had eaten the precise amounts of the nutrients needed to correct the imbalance we imposed on it, and once that had been achieved, they all selected an identical diet—which maintained the balanced nutritional state. The term *nutritional wisdom* was at the time in vogue. Here we had seen nutritional genius. The cockroaches had behaved like nutrient-seeking missiles.

Shortly after, Stephen left science to pursue a career in the church. We have yet to tell Richard Dawkins.

Thanks to the cockroaches, we had become more confident that nutrient balancing was not an arcane ability confined to a few species. But these intriguing if unpleasant creatures were of interest mainly to researchers in pest control. To extend our test of the generality of nutrient balancing in nature, we next turned to species that were widely believed not to balance their nutrient intake.

The perfect choice was predators. According to foraging theory, these animals would have no need to feed selectively to balance their nutrient intake because the foods of predators—the bodies of other animals—were thought to contain the same mix of nutrients as the animal eating them (making the axiom "You are what you eat" the literal truth). As a result, scientists believed, it should be effortless for predatory animals to consume a properly balanced diet, while we creatures who eat more than one thing would have to work harder at it.

If this were true, it had obvious implications for our theory of nutrient balancing: it would fail to apply to the very large group of animals that obtain their nutrition from eating other animals.

We needed to test this. A perfect opportunity arose when David examined the PhD thesis of a young Danish researcher, David Mayntz, on spiders.

That was an interesting experience. David's own PhD defense, at Oxford University, was a serious affair, involving five hours of earnest discussion and argument with a small expert panel of examiners. Only after that was a decision made about whether the candidate had passed. If this is likened (with some justification) to a no-holds-barred kickboxing match, then a Danish PhD defense is more like the charade of professional wrestling. The candidate sits with the examiners at the front of a room, in this case on a stage, before a public audience usually including family and friends. By this point, it has already been decided that the thesis has passed, and the main purpose of the questioning is entertainment: it gives the candidate an opportunity to demonstrate their expertise and prowess in debating their research topic.

With his recently earned PhD degree, David Mayntz moved to Oxford to work with us applying Nutritional Geometry to predators. We designed an experiment like the one Stephen Jones had done on cockroaches. In a stroke of genius, David Mayntz suggested that we include in the experiment not just one but three species of predator, each differing in their hunting strategies. This presented a very stern test of our theory.

The first species, a ground beetle, moves around its environment searching for prey in much the same way that cockroaches forage. In the wild, these animals, theoretically at least, could select among the prey that they capture and eat.

The second was a wolf spider. Like the beetle, this species is mobile; but rather than searching for prey, it sits and waits for dinner to come to it.

The third species was least mobile of all: a web-building spider, which invests in building a trap for its prey.

We reasoned that if predators *did* balance their nutrient intake, the mobile beetle, which has opportunity to encounter many different prey types, would be the most likely to do so. The web-building spider, which has little choice over what gets trapped in its web, would be least likely to do so. The sit-and-wait predator would be somewhere in between because, even though it has little influence over which prey come within striking range, it can easily move among hunting spots to influence its opportunities.

We tested each species in an experiment that matched its ecology. We offered the mobile beetles a buffet-style test, like the cockroach experiment, in which the different test foods were available together. In the wild, web-building spiders have to make do with whatever happens to wander into their trap. So, rather than offer them a choice of prey in our experiment, we gave each a single victim that was either high or low in the nutrient they were lacking—fat or protein—and measured how the spiders responded to each. Like web builders, in nature, sit-and-wait predators can choose where they lay their ambush but not which prey come within striking distance. They, too, were tested on a single prey that was either high or low in the nutrient they lacked.

(How, you might wonder, did we get prey that differed in the balance of fat and protein they contained? The answer is that we raised the prey—flies—in our lab and gave *them* different diets. We designed some diets to make flies fat, and these chubby insects provided fatty meals for their predators, while other flies grew lean on low-fat, high-protein feed.)

The roving beetles behaved much like the cockroaches: if they had previously been restricted to low-fat prey, they specifically selected high-fat foods, and if previously restricted to low protein, they chose high protein. The sit-and-wait predator chose its nutrients by eating different amounts of the prey it had been offered, depending on its composition: the spider ate more of fatty animals if fat was needed and more of lean ones when protein was needed.

The web-building spider did the most remarkable thing of all. Its way of feeding is to inject into prey a cocktail of digestive enzymes, then suck out a soup of predigested nutrients from the body, discarding the remaining solids. We found that the discarded part of the body was particularly depleted in the nutrient most needed by the predator, suggesting that they could tailor the cocktail of enzymes they injected into prey in order to meet specific nutrient needs.

David Mayntz's experiment had shown not only that all three predators balanced their nutrient intake but also that the mechanism for this differed with different foraging strategies. Some selected among prey, some regulated the amount of a specific prey they ate, and others selectively extracted nutrients from whatever prey was captured. It was looking increasingly unlikely that we would find a significant number of animal species that *didn't* balance their nutrient intake.

Usually, when people think about predators, their thoughts are not on invertebrates like beetles and spiders but on charismatic examples like lions, tigers, and sharks. Did they, too, carefully mix foods in the exact proportions to balance their nutrient intakes? It seems ridiculous to consider a lion or shark sizing up its prey for body composition, but then in recent years our research had presented a series of surprises.

Even more ridiculous was the thought that we could do locust-like lab experiments on man-eaters. Happily, many of us share our houses with predators that are somewhat less likely to eat their experimenter.

An opportunity arose when we were contacted by Adrian Hewson-Hughes, a research scientist at a prominent pet food company. Adrian had come across our work and wondered whether it applied to domestic cats and dogs. It was the practical implications that interested Adrian and us, too, but we also saw a wonderful opportunity to answer the question of whether vertebrate predators balance their diets.

At the first opportunity, we visited Adrian and his team and helped to design geometric experiments to test the theory. It was some years before the experiments were done, but the results were well worth the wait. In all cases, we found that nutrient balance is the strongest determinant of domestic pets' food choice and eating behavior. We also found some fascinating differences between these species that relate to their evolutionary history.

Cats selected a diet with 52 percent of energy from protein, which is a typical value for wild predators, including the ancestors of domesticated cats and wolves. Dogs—all five breeds we studied—selected a diet of only 25 to 35 percent protein, much lower than the diets of the wolves from which dogs were domesticated and more like that of omnivores. This suggests that dogs have been altered in the process of domestication to a greater extent than have cats.

Why? Several years later, David witnessed the most likely reason.

He was at Tuanan research station, in the swamp forests of Borneo, studying wild orangutans. At the station were both cats and dogs. Tuanan is no holiday destination (as we will see in Chapter 9), and like everybody else based there, both species had their job to do. Cats were there to catch mice, which otherwise would threaten the precious food supplies, and dogs to alert the researchers when wild animals like leopards approached.

David noticed two important things about these working animals. The first, if he didn't know better, might have seemed an injustice: only the dogs were fed. The cats were left to fend for themselves, which improved their performance in pest control.

The second is *what* the dogs were fed. The research station is extremely remote—to get there, the team drove for several hours over rough roads, then traveled for several more on a large motorized wooden canoe up a river through the forest, like a scene from Joseph Conrad's *Heart of Darkness*. Space on the boat was at a premium. The human passengers were tightly packed, in physical contact with each other, and all remaining space was filled with valuable supplies and research equipment.

There were, therefore, no cans or bags of fancy-flavored dog meals aboard, and none made their way to the station. The dogs relied on a diet like that of their domesticated ancestors since before the invention of "dog foods," even before the invention of agriculture: our table scraps.

And this is the likely reason why domestic cats and dogs prefer different macronutrient mixtures. Being small and often valued for their ability to control rodent populations, cats have continued to hunt and eat prey throughout their evolution and domestication. As larger animals, an important (and probably early) priority in the domestication of dogs was to breed out the hunting tendencies for which wolves are renowned, in the interests of human and livestock safety. Instead, dogs were forced to rely on our table scraps, which are much higher in carbs and fat than usual carnivore fare, and therefore became more similar in their nutrient selection to us omnivores, their owners.

Another result of the dietary switch of dogs is that they have developed an ability to digest starch more efficiently than other carnivores through evolving an increased number of genes for producing amylase (starch-digesting) enzymes. Over time, as we'll see in Chapter 10, humans underwent a similar evolutionary change in response to agricultural production of starchy crops, such as grains. This shows how a shared environment, in this case the carb-rich world occasioned by farming, can produce similar changes in different species, a process called *convergent evolution*. Our dogs have become more human.

Still, even though they got the proportions of macronutrients in their diet spot on, some dog breeds we tested overshot the mark when it came to the amount they ate. In fact, they ingested far more calories than our calculations suggested they needed. It won't come as a surprise to anyone who owns one that Labradors ate nearly twice what was necessary. A likely evolutionary reason is that their wolf ancestors are adapted to a "feast and famine" lifestyle in which they compete with others in the pack to gorge on occasional kills, then go long periods without eating. In the context of our story, though, it holds an important message: even gluttons must balance their nutrient intake.

It seemed we had learned something important from the impressive nutrient balancing we observed in predators, but it also got us thinking. Prevailing foraging theory had predicted that predators would have no need to balance their nutrient intake because animal tissues are already balanced to meet the needs of carnivores. But, why then *do* predators feed selectively to balance their nutrient intake? In this, they behaved much the same way we had observed for herbivores and omnivores.

Then we realized—the initial premise was wrong.

Foraging theory erred in assuming that the body composition of animals is constant. In fact, we realized, there's a great deal of variation depending on diet, season, health, and many other factors. We saw an example above: by changing the diets of flies, we were able to create fat and thin prey for the spiders in David Mayntz's experiment. Think also about the fat content of our own species—it can range from a mere 2 percent of body weight in Olympic athletes to over 50 percent among the obese, equivalent to the difference between dry lentils and creamy ranch dressing. In a *single species*!

Even more important, no single dietary composition would be optimal throughout a predator's entire lifetime. This is because, like any animal, the nutrient needs of predators change depending on whether they are still growing or fully grown and reproducing; healthy or diseased; young or old; active or sedentary; and so forth. Therefore, like herbivores and omnivores, predators feed selectively to optimize their diets for specific circumstances, and the wide variety of prey available provides plenty of opportunity to do so.

This was illustrated by another study that we did with David Mayntz. It involved the same species of ground beetle from the initial experiment together with spiders, but with a twist. This time, David went out into the field and collected beetles immediately after they emerged from a long hibernation through the cold Danish winter, then brought them into the lab to study.

During hibernation, they eat nothing, living off the fat stores they have accumulated in advance. We knew, therefore, that they would be very lean when collected and urgently in need of some fattening up. Our question, then, was whether this influenced their food choices.

At first, they selected a fat-rich diet. Then, as their own fat stores grew, they gradually toned down that nutrient's intake and ate more protein. This, too, was no coincidence: at that stage they were preparing to reproduce, which in insects is a protein-intensive process.

The message, of course, is that there is no such thing as a single balanced diet for these beetles—their needs change across the life cycle. Nutrient selection even changes with an animal's activity level. Another student working with us, Louise Firth, made locusts fly for differing periods and then found that the ones who had flown the longest selected a diet higher in carbohydrate than protein, since carbs provide the fuel used in flight.

For (almost) all animals, then, predators included, feeding is a process of a wobbly gun barrel aimed at a moving target. Specialized stabilizing mechanisms—in the form of interacting appetites—are needed to collaborate if there is to be any hope of success. Exceptions are likely to be few, restricted to very special cases.

One exception is the food designed specifically to meet *all* the nutrient needs of an animal: mammalian milk. Particularly fascinating is the Australian tammar wallaby. In this species, the young live inside a pouch on the mother's belly and therefore have no opportunity to eat anything other than milk. But this is a *single* food only in name: the wallaby mother's milk undergoes complex changes in composition over time, modifying the mixes of nutrients needed for the specific stage of the baby's development. For example, differing mixes of amino acids are produced to enable the growth of the brain, lungs, nails, and fur. More than that, females may simultaneously be carrying around two young of different ages. When that happens, each has a dedicated nipple producing the cocktail of nutrients it needs for its specific age. We predict, though, that when the young leave their privileged position in the pouch to fend for themselves, feeding mechanisms would be no different from other species. They, too, will have to develop nutrient-specific appetites.

We had answered our original question: nutrient balancing *is* widespread across species and not an exception. Our experiments had shown that it occurs in herbivores, omnivores, and carnivores, both domesticated and undomesticated, and we had rethought foraging theory to explain why.

But as biologists with a habit of watching animals in the wild, we realized that only in certain circumstances was nature obliging enough to provide the abundance and diversity of foods that could always ensure a nutritionally balanced diet. Often, in the real world, it is impossible for an animal to eat the correct amount of all nutrients. Such imbalance was so common, we suspected, that animals would have to have a Plan B—meaning that their appetite systems would need a way to respond when getting the desired nutrients was impossible. They would need a response that could compromise and help them balance eating too much of one thing against too little of others.

This was exactly the question we had set about to answer in the locust experiment: What is the nature of Plan B for a locust? The answer was that they ultimately prioritized protein over other nutrients and would even extend their development time and become obese if those were what it took to get to a target intake of protein. What, we wondered, would Plan B be for humans? As far as we knew, the question had never been asked, let alone answered. We decided to find out, and what happened next set the direction for the rest of our careers.

CHAPTER 5 AT A GLANCE

1. Even the most unlikely animal species—from cockroaches to cats—can use their multiple appetites to mix a balanced diet, like nutrient-seeking missiles.
2. However, as we saw in Chapter 3, these appetites compete when the diet is imbalanced—and in locusts, protein wins the competition.
3. What about humans?

6

The Protein Leverage Hypothesis

ONE DAY IN 2001, AN UNDERGRADUATE STUDENT named Rachel Batley knocked on the door to Steve's office. "I'm looking for ideas for my Honours research project," she announced, "preferably something on people."

This was an unusual request. Not the bit about seeking an Honours project, as that was a compulsory part of the Oxford undergraduate degree in zoology, but rather wanting to study the human animal instead of insects, badgers, or something more zoological.

When it comes to research of this kind, people are trouble.

"Well, yes," Steve replied, "as it happens, there's a locust experiment we've been *wanting* to run on humans . . ."

The elegant simplicity of the locust results had got us thinking about ourselves—or more specifically, whether we humans really *are* as different and complex as we'd like to believe, or if beneath all the freewill and cultural fanfare we are just like locusts, with a few powerful and ancient drivers determining what we eat and how much. And, if macronutrient appetites are among these basic biological forces, another question arose: Are fats or carbs the main culprits in the rising tide of obesity, as they are commonly portrayed to be? After all, the rising intake of calories that has fueled the global obesity epidemic has been consumed as fats and carbs, certainly not as protein. Protein intake has remained pretty much the same for decades.

But getting an accurate record of what people eat has bedeviled the study of human nutrition since the beginning. Most research has relied on subjects self-reporting what they have eaten over previous days. The trouble is, we forget. We also cheat and lie to ourselves as much as to others. There's a story told by nutrition scientist John de Castro, who thought he'd cracked the problem by having his subjects take a photo of each meal. By using these images as *aides-mémoire* to help fill out their food questionnaires, surely there'd be no chance of any errors.

Or so he thought—mistakenly. He called it the "missing brownie" effect. There it sat in the photo in all its rich, calorific deliciousness, yet the participant had failed to list the chocolate brownie on the food diary spreadsheet, unlike the fruit, vegetables, and lean chicken on the adjacent plate, all of which were faithfully recorded.

Rather than relying on dietary recall, it would be more accurate to treat human subjects as we did locusts—keep them imprisoned in isolation for an extended period with nothing to eat but their ration of a single, dry experimental gruel. This would certainly allow a reliable measure of food intake but would not have people banging down the doors to volunteer as participants.

Happily, Rachel offered a wonderful solution. Her family owned an isolated chalet in the Swiss Alps—a convivial place to be and safely far from the nearest supermarket or bar. She recruited a group of ten friends and family and took them for a week without caffeine, alcohol, or chocolate, to become human locusts.

Here's how the experiment worked: for the first two days, participants ate whatever they liked, as much as they liked, from a buffet of meat, fish, eggs, dairy, breads, fruit, vegetables, and so on. Everything was weighed, and food composition tables were used to look up the protein, carbs, and fats in each item. All that data was recorded for every meal and snack each person consumed.

Then, on days three and four, the participants were divided into two groups, and their choices were narrowed. One group got a high-protein buffet—meat and fish, eggs, some low-fat dairy, a little fruit and vegetables; the other was fed a low-protein but high-carb and high-fat diet of everything *but* meat, fish, and eggs—lots of pasta, bread, and cereal choices, even dessert. Again, all subjects ate as much as they wanted, and choices were recorded for calories and macronutrients. Exactly as we had done for locusts, spiders, cockroaches, and other animals previously.

Following two days of that, they were returned for two days to the original buffet offering choices of all foods, after which their task was complete, and they were released back into the wild. We, meanwhile, had some new numbers to crunch. We needed some serious clear time, and the day-to-day demands of busy academic life in Oxford were making that difficult.

In July 2002, we both decamped to Berlin with our families for a year as Fellows at the Wissenschaftskolleg (Institute for Advanced Study). Each year, the governing board of the Institute invites forty academics from around the world and across disciplines to come together as a ready-made community. That year our number included writers and composers, biologists, political economists, philosophers, ethnographers, and more. One among us, the Hungarian writer Imre Kertész, won the Nobel Prize in Literature that October. (We claim no credit for that but enjoyed the celebration.)

Our office in the Villa Jaffé was not unaccustomed to the animal side of human nature. In the Second World War, it had been seized by the Nazis under the Nuremberg Laws to house Hermann Goering's Reich Hunting Association. After the war, it became home to a button factory before being returned to the family of the previous owners, who by then were living in Israel.

We began the year by delving deep into the results of the Swiss chalet study. We found that when allowed to select their diet, in the first phase of the experiment, the participants did a good job of eating the expected number of calories, at a ratio of around 18 percent protein—exactly as you would expect humans to do, as 15 to 20 percent is the typical value that studies have suggested for people from all around the world. As an aside, this is very similar to the macronutrient ratio that Caley had observed Stella the baboon to select over the thirty-day observation period, which was 17 percent protein.

Strikingly, in the second phase of the experiment, when the students were divided into either high-protein or high-carbs and high-fats groups, everyone maintained their protein intake to a similar level as in the free-choice period. To do this, those confined to the high-carb and high-fat diet had to eat 35 percent more total calories to reach their target intake of protein. By contrast, those assigned the high-protein menu ended up eating 38 percent *fewer* calories than before.

Clearly, our college students responded just like our locusts had done: the appetite for protein seemed to have determined the total consumption of food.

But, we were well aware, this was just a suggestion rather than an answer. Humans are complex, numerous, and diverse, and all we had done was show that this small group of college students, under controlled circumstances, ate in a certain way. Could the results be explained other than by the similarity between human and locust feeding tendencies?

For example, we hadn't investigated how our human subjects ate prior to the experiment; perhaps, by chance, the two groups that we had separated had different eating habits to begin with. Also—unlike the locusts, which we held in isolation in plastic boxes—the students ate in a highly social setting, leaving them vulnerable to the influence of their friends' choices. And while animals stop eating whenever they like, we humans feel compelled to finish everything on our plates, out of politeness or the wish to not waste food. There's even a scientific term for it—*completion compulsion.*

Even with its potential flaws, Rachel's experiment had provided some very exciting results. Given such similar behaviors in locusts and humans, we were now confident in setting up the following hypothesis:

> In a protein-poor but energy-rich food environment, humans will overeat carbs and fats to try to reach their protein target. However, when the only available diet is high in protein, humans will underconsume carbs and fats.

The implications were massive. Assuming no change in calories burned through activity, a high-carb and high-fat diet would eventually lead to weight gain, and the high-protein one, to loss. Depending on one's individual circumstance, either of those outcomes might be desirable. But either way, the top priority in every instance seemed to be to consume a set amount of protein—not too little and not too much. That's the power of protein to leverage everything else that we eat.

If further study bore these findings out, it would represent an entirely new and potentially groundbreaking approach to certain critical questions—among them, why had obesity, and the serious diseases that came with it, arisen in epidemic proportions across much of the globe over recent decades?

Up until this point, most considerations of what caused us to be so newly overweight focused on the two macronutrients contributing excess calories in the human diet—carbs and fats. Protein made up only around 15 percent of our total calorie intake, and the amount eaten had hardly changed for decades in populations all over the world (at least those with stable access to food). Sure, there have been big shifts in patterns of consumption of protein-containing foods—increases in demand for red meat with economic development in some countries, reliance on increased poultry in the Western diet with the industrialization of their production, and so on. However, the total amount of protein people ate, summed across all foods containing it, whether plant- or animal-derived, was utterly stable over decades and across populations around the world.

Unsurprisingly, based on all that data, the prevailing view among public health experts was that protein must be blameless in the obesity epidemic. After all, the excess calorie intake that had driven the world's expanding waistline came from fat and carbs.

But our work on locusts, and now humans, had suggested another explanation: it was precisely *because* of that constancy in protein intake, we saw, that it deserved closer scrutiny.

By attempting to maintain a target intake, had our protein appetite driven us to consume excess calories in a world in which the food supply had become increasingly dominated by fats and carbs?

In the years 1961 to 2000, according to the Food and Agriculture Organization of the United Nations database of nutrient availability (which is not identical to consumption but close enough), the average diet composition in the United States changed significantly—it fell from 14 percent protein to 12.5 percent. The other macronutrients, fats and carbs, of course, made up the balance. Given that shift, the only way Americans could have maintained their target protein consumption was to increase total calorie intake by 13 percent—creating an energy (Calorie) surplus and associated weight gain. Which is pretty much what was happening, though no one was paying attention.

We wrote up the results of the Swiss chalet study, which were published in 2003, and began drafting a second publication, which took two more years to appear. It was titled *Obesity: The Protein Leverage Hypothesis.* Both were met with disquiet and delay by the human nutrition community.

In 2005, Steve spoke at Cambridge University, and at a dinner afterward, a senior figure in the field said that he wanted us to know that he had stalled our Protein Leverage Hypothesis paper in the review stage, before it could be published. Why would he do such a thing? He said he believed we were probably right, but we had to understand how hard it would be for those scientists like him in the human nutrition field to realize they had missed something that now seemed so obvious and had been beaten to it by two insect biologists.

We treasure that admission. Such generosity of spirit is the hallmark of the very best scientists.

Upon returning to Oxford after our year in Berlin, both of us felt unshackled—the barnacles of day-to-day academic life had dropped away. Within months, of course, they began to reattach; so, we escaped again—David to a position in New Zealand and Steve to an Australian Research Council Federation Fellowship at the University of Sydney, specifically designed to repatriate Australian scientists who had spent much of their careers abroad. The fellowship was barnacle-free—the only obligation was that fellows would build new and exciting research programs. Heaven.

Among the first projects we wished to tackle in Sydney was a beefed-up version (no pun intended) of the Swiss chalet experiment. This time, we wanted to control for two wobbly aspects of the earlier study. The first was that we hadn't considered palatability differences among the experimental diets. What if people didn't like the taste of our high-protein menus, and this explained why they ate less on those days? Or, if those on the low-protein/high-carb and -fat diet liked their food so much that they ate more than they really wanted? In other words, maybe the constant protein intake was purely a coincidence.

Or, what if the difference in consumption between the free choice and restricted phases was due to the differing numbers of foods available? In the eat-anything-you-like phase, there were twice as many foods to choose from than in the restricted phase. Maybe variety influenced what everyone ate?

This time we wanted to provide the same number of foods in all the menus but somehow disguise the different protein contents and also match the choices for pleasantness. A great deal of scientific inquiry proceeds this way: once something potentially important has been observed, new experiments are designed to ensure that it is real and doesn't have an alternative explanation.

We recruited a nutrition scientist, Alison Gosby, to help on the project in Sydney. She skillfully and laboriously designed twenty-eight foods from which she compiled menus for breakfast, lunch, dinner, and snacks. All were made in three versions, containing 10, 15, or 25 percent protein, each with the same total energy (calorie) content. These three versions of each food were also matched in palatability, as verified in tests with study subjects.

Alison then recruited twenty-two healthy, lean volunteers and kept them prisoner (like human locusts) for three separate four-day periods in small groups, in hotel-style accommodation in the university's sleep research center. She took them out for an hour's walk each day, supervised so they wouldn't be tempted to sneak off and buy snacks. Subjects thought they were all getting the same menus week after week and weren't told what the experiment was aiming to discover. We had all bases covered—palatability, energy density, variety, availability. Any differences in the amounts eaten were highly likely to be due to the protein content of their menus. Would our subjects behave as the students in the Swiss chalet did and eat more energy on a low-protein diet?

They certainly did—they consumed 12 percent more calories during the week on the lowest-protein diet. That 12 percent total calorie increase is more than enough to explain the entire global obesity epidemic. We had created a microcosm of how the world now eats and got the same alarming result.

Intriguingly, most of the extra calories came not from people consuming bigger meals but instead through snacking. We offered both sweet and savory snacks, and you might expect that the sweets were to blame for all the extra calories—but you'd be wrong. The increase came almost exclusively from the savory-flavored snacks—those that tasted of umami. If you remember from our discussion of appetite, umami is the signal that a food contains protein. On the high-carb/fat and low-protein diet, our subjects were being fooled into eating things that only *tasted* like protein but in fact were highly processed carbs.

We next had an opportunity to run a version of the Sydney experiment in Jamaica, thanks to meeting Professor Terrence Forrester from the University of the West Indies, through colleague Professor Sir Peter Gluckman from Auckland, where David was then based.

In 2011, David and his PhD student, Claudia Martinez-Cordero, traveled to Kingston to help Terrence and his PhD student, Claudia Campbell, set up the experiment. It was, in most respects, like the Sydney experiment, with one difference. We also planned to measure whether humans selected an intake target, just as we had done for locusts, cockroaches, and other creatures, and if so, what mix of macronutrients did this consist of?

Alison later traveled to Jamaica with her hard-won protein-disguised recipes and menus—only to find that the locals wouldn't touch them.

"You don't have that for breakfast!" was a typical reaction. "Why would you have those foods in the same meal?"

What was perfectly acceptable to our Sydney population was unacceptable in the culinary tradition of Jamaica. Alison had to start again and design new meals, but it was well worthwhile.

Over the first three days of the experiment, the sixty-three volunteers could freely select any diet they wished from three available menus, containing foods of 10, 15, and 25 percent protein. In other words, if they wished, they could have mixed a diet anywhere between 10 and 25 percent protein. Yet all subjects combined the foods from the various menus to select a diet very close to 15 percent protein, the value similar to what most human populations across the globe eat. In the second part of the experiment, where each subject was given a diet of *only* 10, 15, or 25 percent protein, results were the same as the Sydney trial: study participants ate more food and energy overall on the low-protein diet. Over the course of the five-day experiment, they even showed the beginnings of weight gain.

It was looking like our animal research had potentially led us to solve a very big human problem, one of the biggest there is—what has caused our species to accumulate levels of body fat unprecedented in its two-million-year history. But the trouble with science, which is also its beauty, is that with most discoveries come new questions that need to be answered. And this was no exception.

CHAPTER 6 AT A GLANCE

1. Humans, like locusts, prioritize eating a target amount of protein.
2. In a protein-poor but energy-rich world, we overeat carbs and fats to try to reach our protein target, risking obesity.
3. When the diet is high in protein, we underconsume carbs and fats to avoid overeating protein.
4. This is why high-protein diets can help you lose weight. But why would we risk eating too few calories to avoid eating too much protein?

7

Why Not Just Eat More Protein?

IT LOOKED AS IF WE HAD JUST DISCOVERED SOMEthing important for solving the human obesity mystery. Simply increase the proportion of protein in the diet, and we won't eat enough else to cause obesity, diabetes, heart disease, or any of the other associated health problems. But if that were true, why would nature have put an upper limit on our appetite for protein? Something didn't add up.

Why too *little* protein matters is pretty obvious—as we saw earlier, this nutrient provides the primary source of nitrogen needed to build, maintain, and repair our bodies and to allow us to reproduce. We need enough protein to live.

But why should we be so unwilling to *over*eat it—to the extent that on a diet containing a high percentage of protein, you'll eat less food than you need to maintain your body weight? Yes, losing weight might be welcome to many of us today, but throughout our species' existence, this has never been a desirable outcome. In fact, just the opposite—the challenge was in getting enough to eat in order to survive. A dietary regimen that guaranteed weight loss would have been suicidal.

It seems, then, as though our appetites are telling us we're better off eating too few calories, at the risk of running out of energy, than we would be ingesting too much protein. This alone suggests that there is something seriously undesirable about excess protein intake. Highly tuned control systems, such as that protein appetite, do not evolve by accident. Indeed, if characteristics are not useful for survival and reproduction, they wither and are eventually lost. "Use it or lose it" is a good maxim for evolution.

There was also evidence that very high intakes of protein are bad for you. This was famously seen in the phenomenon of "rabbit starvation."

This has nothing to do with starving rabbits. Rather, it's the lesson learned by the Greely Arctic Expedition of 1881–1884, during which nineteen of the twenty-five explorers who had gone there to conduct scientific research died.

Rabbit, like most wild animals, is an extremely low-fat meat—around 8 percent, compared to 28 percent for lamb and 32 for beef and pork. The rest is protein, with carbs essentially absent. If you were to eat nothing but rabbits, the very high ratio of protein to fat and carbs would soon cause what has been termed *protein poisoning*—a rare form of malnutrition caused by too much protein compared to the other two macronutrients. Arctic explorer Vilhjalmur Stefansson, who experienced it himself, wrote: "Rabbit eaters, if they have no fat from another source—beaver, moose, fish—will develop diarrhea in about a week, with headache, lassitude, and vague discomfort."

Of course, there was no abundance of rabbits (or anything else edible) during that fateful expedition to the Arctic. According to Stefansson, those deaths among the men in the Greely venture had to do with what was believed to have been cannibalism once they ran out of food (shades of our Mormon crickets). By the time the human fatalities were consumed, their bodies had so little fat that they might as well have been rabbits. Or so the theory held.

Charles Darwin himself noted the need for eating sufficient fat and carbs compared to protein in *The Voyage of the Beagle*, where he wrote:

> I had now been several days without tasting anything besides meat: I did not at all dislike this new regimen; but I felt as if it would only have agreed with me with hard exercise. I have heard that patients in England, when desired to confine themselves exclusively to an animal diet, even with the hope of life before their eyes, have hardly been able to endure it. Yet the Gaucho in the Pampas, for months together, touches nothing but beef. But they eat, I observe, a very large proportion of fat, which is of a less animalized nature; and they particularly dislike dry meat, such as that of the agouti.

But the human target intake for protein (15 percent or so of total calories) is nowhere near the 40 to 50 percent levels needed to cause sickness. Any ill effects of protein consumption above the target intake must, therefore, be subtler than severe diarrhea and death.

We also know that some animals have evolved not just to tolerate high levels of protein in the diet but to require them. This means that, whatever the challenges of eating high levels of protein are, they can be overcome, in time, by evolution. As we explained in Chapter 5, we conducted experiments on a range of predatory species, including cats, dogs, spiders, and beetles, and found that these animals require 30 to 60 percent of their calories in the form of protein, compared to our paltry 15 percent. This of course makes sense, as these animals have evolved mainly to eat other animals—which are high in protein.

But even predators avoid eating more protein than their intake target if they are able and display serious cravings for fat as protein becomes too concentrated in the diet. When fat is scarce, populations of predatory animals can decline radically. This can be seen in the seabird populations of the North Atlantic, which have plummeted over recent decades because of serious declines in the stocks of oily fish thanks to overfishing. The birds are left to feed on leaner, more protein-rich prey species that do not sustain the energy reserves needed for flight and migration.

It was becoming clear that we needed to find a way to understand the costs of eating too much protein relative to other nutrients and to compare these ills, whatever they are, with those of eating too little protein. Then Steve had a chance encounter at a party . . .

It was 2005, and Steve and his family had just moved from Oxford to Sydney and were settling into a rental house. The new neighbors were hosting a street party and invited them. Late in the evening, Steve was chatting with a new acquaintance, David Le Couteur, who turned out to be a professor of gerontology and a clinician at Sydney University. When he found out that Steve was a biologist, he asked whether he would give a lecture on nutrition at an international conference on the biology of healthy aging. Steve said yes, but the next morning he awoke asking himself, "What have I done? I know nothing about the biology of aging . . ."

Steve contacted David in New Zealand, and we started to look closely at the scientific literature. As we read, we became increasingly intrigued—and perplexed.

The likelihood that we will suffer from a suite of diseases, including obesity, type 2 diabetes, heart disease and stroke, dementia, and cancer, rises steeply and in lockstep with age. There is something about the process of growing old that seems to predispose us to these chronic ailments, leaving us many years (on average) of poor health before we die.

At the time, in 2005, there was one big idea about the link between diet and the biology of aging: that by restricting calorie intake by up to 40 percent—for humans, around 1,000 fewer calories per day—lifespan can be extended in a whole range of species. This was not about avoiding obesity by eating less but, rather, slowing the fundamental biology of the aging process itself.

The study of calorie restriction and aging has a long and colorful history. Luigi Cornaro (1464–1566) was a wealthy Venetian nobleman who indulged in a life of excesses, including gluttony, until middle age, when his health had deteriorated so badly he thought he was dying. On medical advice, he adopted a calorie-restricted diet, eating only a few hundred grams of food each day. Feeling spry, in his eighties he wrote a book titled *Sure and Certain Methods of Attaining a Long and Healthful Life: With Means of Correcting a Bad Constitution, &c.*, where he attributed his longevity to a temperate life and eating as little as possible. He is thought to have endured to the age of 102.

In 1935, Clive McCay and colleagues at Cornell University published a landmark paper on rats, titled "The Effect of Retarded Growth upon the Length of Life Span and upon the Ultimate Body Size," which provided the first compelling research evidence that calorie restriction prolongs life. McCay's calorie-restricted rats grew more slowly but lived longer than their better-fed counterparts.

Since that time there have been many reports on different organisms—from yeast cells and worms to flies and monkeys—showing that calorie restriction extends lifespan. There is a downside, however: in all these species, living longer has been associated with having fewer offspring. This trade-off between lifespan and offspring led to the idea that investing energy in one process comes at the expense of the other, with organisms spending their calories and resources either on living longer or on having and raising babies. Another idea was that there are direct costs of reproducing—wear and tear, so to speak—that directly shorten lifespan. New, sleep-deprived parents could well believe that idea.

For many modern-day humans, however, the idea of fewer children and longer life expectancy would seem like the best of both worlds, and the falling birth rates and increased longevity in developed nations bear this notion out.

An early opportunity to study calorie restriction in humans came with the Biosphere 2 venture in Arizona. Famously, this was a closed ecological system—a greenhouse containing a miniature rain forest, a desert, a little ocean, a mangrove swamp, a savanna, and a small farm. In 1991, renowned calorie restriction researcher Roy Walford from UCLA was one of eight people who shut themselves into Biosphere 2 for two years, during which the "Biospherians" could only produce enough food for a low-calorie diet. Walford reported that they lost weight and had similar beneficial metabolic health changes (such as reduced blood pressure and better control of blood glucose), the same as had been seen previously in calorie-restricted rats.

This is all very interesting, but here's why we were puzzled. Among all the research publications on calorie restriction, nobody had ever examined the role of each of the three macronutrients separately. Given our focus, of course, we wondered whether living longer was caused by eating fewer total calories—or if the *source* of those calories was what mattered. In other words, what is the effect of protein, fats, and carbs on aging—not only singly but as mixtures?

Steve delivered a provocative talk to that healthy aging conference, questioning the evidence behind the conclusion that calorie restriction prolongs life. He argued that there were insufficient grounds to conclude that total calories were key and that it remained possible that the source of those calories mattered more than their number. In fact, he told his audience, there was evidence from studies using rodents and flies that restriction of protein and certain amino acids (such as methionine and branched-chain amino acids) were perhaps more important than the number of calories eaten. He did not expect to be invited back.

But Steve's listeners took no offense and in fact encouraged us to look afresh at calorie restriction through our Nutritional Geometry lens. We set out a plan to disentangle the effect of calories from nutrients and concluded that the most feasible way to start such a massive experimental task was by using small, short-lived animals—yes, insects.

We turned to the fruit fly, *Drosophila*, which is the model insect used for research into the biology of aging, as well as being famous for its use in the study of genetics and molecular biology. Fruit flies are a surprisingly good model for understanding human health. Three-quarters of human disease-causing genes have related versions in the fly. We also share the genes controlling lifespan and aging with flies, but the average lifespan of a fly is so brief that we could conduct an entire birth-to-death experiment in a couple of months.

"Bob" was how Kwang-Pum Lee introduced himself in 1999, when he wrote from Korea seeking admission to our lab in Oxford as a PhD student. He also sent beautifully hand-painted cards of butterflies, which showed he was a born entomologist. During his

PhD work, he discovered that when caterpillars are infected with a virus, their food preferences change so that they select a higher ratio of protein to carbs, which is exactly the medicine required to best combat the virus infection. Kwang next traveled to Lancaster in the north of England to work with a colleague, Ken Wilson, to extend this project. Kwang was productive and successful there but found the unremittingly gray weather hard to bear and leapt at the opportunity to come to Sydney to work on a massive fruit fly aging study.

We designed a locust-style experiment in which more than one thousand flies were each given a single experimental food and tracked throughout their entire adult lives. Because fats are a tiny component of the energy budget of fruit flies, we concentrated on protein and carbs, which we mixed into twenty-eight different liquid diets. These included varying protein-to-carb ratios, each at one of four overall dilutions, achieved by adding water.

The experiment took a year of painstaking work to complete. Wrangling one thousand fruit flies is challenging, given that they are not much larger than the period at the end of this sentence.

Fly maggots were first grown on a common lab food in glass bottles. Once fully developed (which only takes a few days), the maggots pupated and then hatched into adult flies. Newly emerged females were placed with males for twenty-four hours to mate, then isolated in their own private glass vials. At the bottom of each vial was a piece of moistened paper onto which the fly could lay her eggs, and at the top was a stopper holding a tiny (five-millionths of a liter) glass straw, filled with one of the twenty-eight experimental diets. Flies soon learned how to feed from the straw with their long, spongy, drinking tube–like mouth, called a *proboscis*.

Daily, when the straws were refilled with fresh food, Kwang and another senior postdoc in the lab, Fiona Clissold (who had designed our straw technique), measured how much each fly had drunk that day. They could also count using a microscope how many eggs—which are minute, white specks—had been laid. After a couple of months at most, the flies died of natural causes.

At the end of the experiment, we knew how much each fly had eaten per day, how long it lived, and how many eggs it had laid.

Now, imagine that you create a graph on which you plotted each fly's intake of protein and carbs as a dot (as shown for locusts in Chapter 3). By the end, you would have a blank sheet on which there is a cloud of one thousand dots. Next, take one thousand pins of differing lengths and assign each pin to represent the lifespan of a fly—the longer it lived, the longer the pin. Finally, take that pin and stick it into the dot showing that fly's nutrient intake. You end up with a forest of one thousand pins of different lengths positioned according to which food each fly ate.

Taken all together, the pin forest will have created what is called a *response landscape*, which is like a three-dimensional map. The shape of that landscape would tell you how fly lifespan overall corresponded to diet. If all pins had been of the same length, the landscape would have been perfectly flat, like a plateau, meaning that no matter what the flies ate, they all lived the same length of time. But if it looked like a mountain range, with pins rising high at some combination of protein and carb intake and then falling into a valley with a different nutrient balance, we would know that the insects' diets did indeed affect their longevity.

To make it a bit easier to visualize, that three-dimensional pin forest could also be turned into a 2-D map using the same trick cartographers use when representing topography: you shade the heads of the pins based on their length—black for longest through gray for intermediate lengths to white for shortest—then look directly down so that long lifespans become dark regions on the graph and shorter lives are light.

With trepidation, we took the food intake data from our flies and began mapping out the one thousand points of nutrient intake on a graph. Next, we input the data on how long the flies lived and how many eggs they laid across their lifetimes.

Throughout our research, the moment when a graph first appears on the computer screen is one of high drama. All that hard work—a year's worth!—could amount to absolutely nothing of statistical significance. The computer might simply say that not a single interesting or conclusive thing has happened. Biology is heartbreakingly like that—all too often, the patterns are hard to see above the noise. Perhaps we asked the wrong questions, or our hypothesis was wrong, or there were unknown technical problems in the experimental procedures.

On this day, we knew what to expect if the conventional view held by the calorie restrictors was correct: as total food intake decreased, down to 60 percent of normal consumption, lifespan should have gone up—regardless of the protein-to-carb balance in the diet.

We pressed the button and waited while the computer calculated the colored surface graphs and associated statistical tables. And then we saw it. The pattern leapt out of the graph, and the conclusion was radical.

Lifespan had virtually nothing to do with total calories consumed and everything to do with the ratio of protein to carbs you ate.

On the next page are the graphs that appeared that day.

Do you see how the lifespan surface is dark up top, on the low-protein and high-carb diets, and then turns pale gray on high-protein, low-carb intake? This means that as the proportion of protein in the diet increased, flies lived progressively *shorter*. And they died soonest on the high-protein, low-carb diets.

But what about reproduction? You can see it yourself in the right-hand graph: the most eggs were laid when flies ate more protein than would have allowed them to live longest. A ratio of one part protein to sixteen parts carbs supported longest lifespan, but

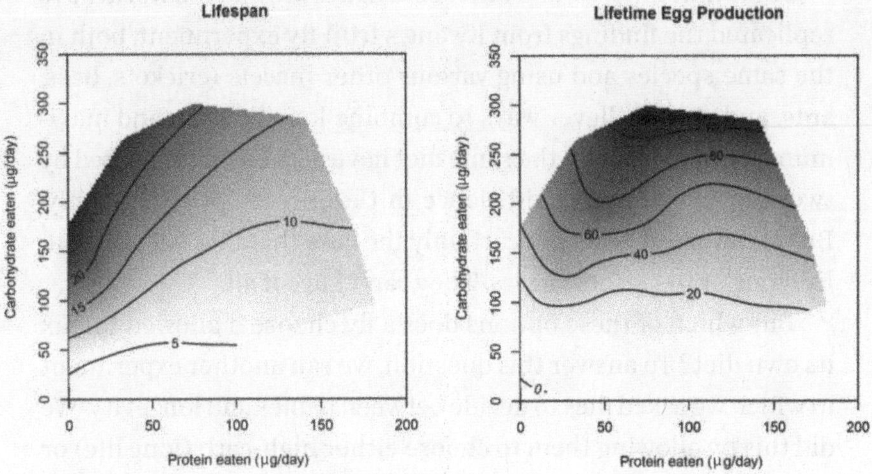

Response maps for lifespan (days) and lifetime egg production for fruit flies kept throughout their lives on one of twenty-eight diets differing in protein and carb content.

a one-to-four ratio was needed to lay the most eggs. But even for reproduction, there was such a thing as too much protein—a ratio of protein to carbs over one to four led to a fall in the number of eggs.

The message for protein was clear—eat a small amount and you will live a long time but not produce many offspring; eat a bit more and you will leave lots of offspring but not live as long; eat even more and you will neither live long *nor* produce many offspring. At least if you happen to be a fruit fly.

Our results had shown convincingly that lifespan and reproduction trade off against one another. It is not, as had been thought, that they compete for a fixed pool of energy and resources or that reproduction itself causes damage that shortens lifespan. No, reproduction and longevity simply have different nutritional requirements. You choose one diet to have many offspring and a different one to delay death. The same diet can't achieve both outcomes.

Eureka.

Since that time, we and other colleagues around the world have replicated the findings from Kwang's fruit fly experiment, both in the same species and using various other insects (crickets, bees, ants, and more). Clever ways to combine long lifespan and maximum reproduction on the same diet have also been discovered by tweaking the amino acid balance in the insects' protein supply. But in nature, it is almost certainly the case that flies eat either to live long or to lay lots of eggs. They can't have it all.

But which of these options does a fly choose if allowed to mix its own diet? To answer this question, we ran another experiment in which we asked flies to decide between babies and longevity. We did this by allowing them to choose either high-carb (long life) or higher-protein (lots of eggs). Here's a clue to what they did: the opposite of what you (or we) would almost certainly choose in this situation. They chose proportions of protein and carbs that supported maximal egg production, not longest lifespan.

In human terms, this would be like eating in a way that allowed us to produce fifteen offspring but then die at age forty. Which is pretty much how we lived until two hundred or so years ago, keeping in mind that most of those children would have died before the age of five. Not much of a bargain today, at least to our eyes.

But fruit flies (and probably all species other than us) care more about the number of genes they leave behind than they do about how long they live. Which is exactly as predicted by Darwinian evolutionary theory—leaving your genes behind is the key to a successful legacy.

Our fruit fly–aging paper created quite a stir when it was published in 2008. Colleagues working on calorie restriction, whose main idea we had just upended, were quick to point out that flies aren't mammals, let alone people. And, of course, they were right. We hadn't shown whether mammals would respond to calories alone or, like flies, to the balance of macronutrients. Nor had we shown that there was a cost to mammals of eating too much protein—either for lifespan *or* for reproduction. One of the anonymous reviewers of our manuscript when it was submitted for peer review before publication had this skeptical reaction:

> In conclusion this manuscript outlines a new approach to the design that has application in the use of dietary restriction with short-lived invertebrate species but I am less convinced of its practical application with rodents.

We had no choice but to take that as a challenge and embark upon a study of creatures a bit more like us than the fly.

CHAPTER 7 AT A GLANCE

1. To discover if there are costs to eating too much protein, we explored the lifelong effects of eating different macronutrient mixtures in an experiment on fruit flies.
2. Living longest and laying most eggs required different diets. Flies lived longest on diets containing low protein and high carbs. High-protein, low-carb diets caused an early death. Flies produced most eggs when fed a higher-protein, lower-carb mixture—but not too high in protein.
3. What about more complex animals—what about mammals?

8

Mapping Nutrition

INSECTS HAD TAUGHT US HOW TO BE NUTRITIONAL cartographers. In the fly experiment, we mapped lifespan and reproduction onto the composition of the diet. The fly experiment also raised a fascinating prospect: Might it be possible to use our Nutritional Geometry to map *all* aspects of health? In other words, to use it to achieve the proper nutrient balance for any desired goal—losing weight, living long, maximizing reproduction, fighting infection, or whatever?

That *would* be useful. To answer this, we had to do what the reviewer of our paper on aging fruit flies had suggested wasn't feasible: run a huge study on animals a good deal closer to humans.

We dreamed up the mega-mouse study still excited by what we had learned from the fruit fly experiment. Our gerontologist friend and Sydney colleague, David Le Couteur, joined the research team, and we recruited young biologist Samantha Solon-Biet to work on the project for her PhD. Sam was well versed in Nutritional Geometry, having done her Honours project in Sydney with Steve on fish feeding behavior (fish are another group of animals with excellent nutritional wisdom, it happens).

We set out to see whether we could map the consequences of nutrient balance on hundreds of lab mice kept throughout their entire lives on one of twenty-five experimental diets designed to differ in macronutrient and fiber content. Unlike flies, mice (like us humans) eat lots of fat, so now we'd have to vary that as well as protein and carbs in their feed. That would multiply the size and complexity of our experiment, making it even more of a challenge to measure all the possible dietary mixtures.

Mice live for several years, not mere months like flies. They are also one hundred thousand times heavier. Whereas we could get by with a few liters of liquid fly food and less than a year to run a thousand-fly experiment, we would need six tons of food and five years of hard work to complete a mouse study. We'd also need a full team of experts able to analyze all the samples collected and then help interpret the results, a process that continues to this day. And a million-dollar grant to do it all.

Mice are sociable creatures, so starting in 2009, we housed newly weaned pups together in same-sex groups of three. A recipe for sexual frustration, but we couldn't complicate things by having them in mixed-sex groups, otherwise in time we'd be swamped with baby mice. They were kept in their home cages and fed pellets of a single experimental food from a metal hopper until they either died of natural causes several years later or else were humanely euthanized in late middle age (around fifteen months) so that we could assess all aspects of their physiology and collect and store their tissues for biochemical analysis.

Those "cull" days were complex affairs, involving a factory line of experts each conducting a single task. First, each mouse was euthanized. (There are strict rules on how this is done, governed by the university's animal ethics committee, which includes laypeople as well as veterinarians and expert scientists.) Then they were scanned to measure body composition (how much fat and lean tissue each had), and samples of muscle were dissected and whisked away for immediate analysis of mitochondrial function, before the rest of the body was passed along the line for organ harvesting. Each organ and tissue sample was prepared for storage—either snap-frozen in liquid nitrogen or fixed in chemicals for later biochemical and microscopic analysis. These samples became an invaluable repository of discoveries yet to be made and others that have already been published.

Thousands of hours of lab work followed. Patterns of gene expression in different tissues and organs were recorded, detailed measures of hundreds of blood chemicals were made, and an inventory of the vast numbers of gut microbes was collated. In addition, records were made of immune markers and the activity of biochemical pathways associated with nutrient-sensing, details of the cellular makeup of tissues were quantified, and much more. Then followed hundreds more hours spent collating and analyzing the vast quantities of data we had generated.

Eventually, all remaining mice had died of natural causes. One, the equivalent of Methuselah, had lived more than four years—twice the usual age.

That experiment alone took five years, start to finish. You may be able to imagine our emotional state when we once again found ourselves sitting in front of a computer screen, waiting for colored graphs and revealing statistics to appear. Another moment spent holding our breath.

Would mice, like flies, have lived longest on low-protein, high-carb diets? That was our hypothesis, but hypotheses exist to be tested. Methuselah was a low-protein, high-carb mouse, but was he just a freak? Exceptions are a fact of life in biology—they are the raw material for evolution. But in research, to put too much emphasis on the peculiar few risks missing the true pattern lying within the results. It also risks finding what you are looking for—the equivalent of seeking the face of the Madonna in the clouds. That's what statistics are for: to look through the mess and variation in the data to the underlying pattern—if one exists.

The graph for lifespan appeared on the screen—in all its glory. It looked remarkably like the response for flies, and the statistics were unequivocal! Check it out on the next page.

The dark region on the graph means the mice on a low-protein, high-carb diet *did* live longer. The fascinating thing was that, just as we'd found in flies, it wasn't protein alone that mattered; low protein needed to be combined with high carb to promote longest life. This would be the equivalent for us of eating less meat, fish, and eggs but more healthy carbs, like low-calorie vegetables, fruits, beans, and whole grains. We also saw that a low-protein, high-fat diet didn't yield the same longevity benefits as a low-protein, high-carb diet. That would be the equivalent of cutting back on meat, fish, eggs, *and* carbs and eating more fatty foods, such as butter, vegetable oils, or fried foods. Again, just as with flies, the shortest-lived mice were those confined to a diet that was high in protein and low in carbs. See how the surface was palest in that region of the graph? An average low-carber mouse would not have a long life, nor would a fly.

And what about reproduction? Here a higher-protein diet was an advantage. For a male mouse to grow a big set of testicles (helpful for promiscuity), or for a female to achieve a big uterus (which can contain a large litter of embryos), they needed a higher-protein

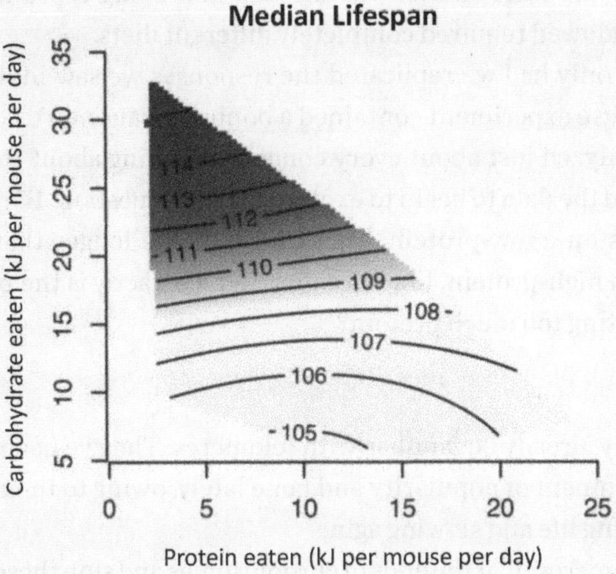

How long mice lived (in weeks) on diets differing in protein and carb content. Fat is not shown here—the ratio of protein to carbs had the biggest effect.

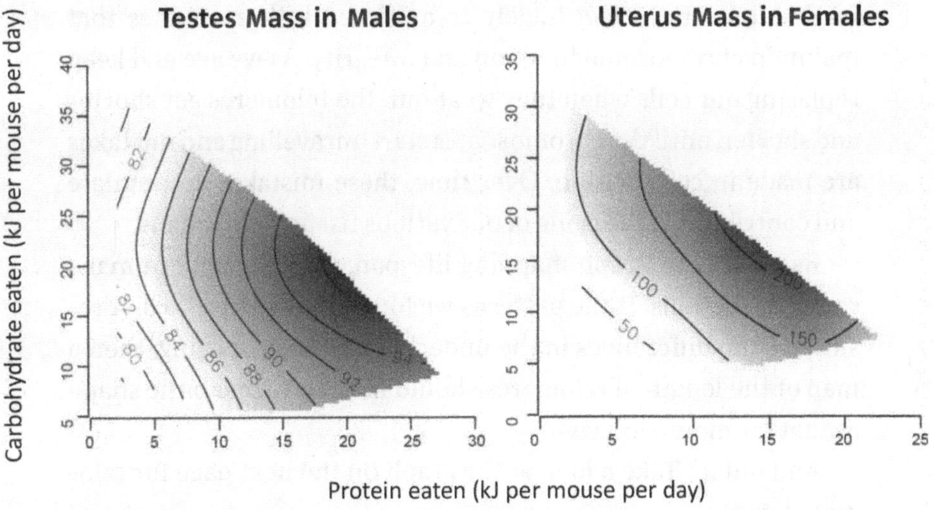

Size of reproductive organs (in mg) in mice fed diets differing in protein and carbs. Again, fat is not shown here.

diet. In the final analysis, living long and being reproductively well-endowed required completely different diets.

Not only had we replicated the responses we saw in flies, but the mouse experiment contained a bonus. Because we'd collected and analyzed just about every conceivable thing about them, we now had the data to begin to explore the next question: *Why* would animals on a low-protein, high-carb diet live longer than those eating a high-protein, low-carb diet? What exactly is the problem with eating too much protein?

You may already be familiar with telomeres. They've been having their moment of popularity and fame lately, owing to their role in extending life and slowing aging.

Telomeres sit at the ends of chromosomes and stop these essential components of cell replication from unravelling as our cells divide. They have been likened to the little plastic bits (called aglets, for what that's worth) that stop the ends of your shoelaces from fraying, but are in fact hugely complicated little machines that maintain chromosome function and integrity. As we age and keep replacing our cells when they wear out, the telomeres get shorter and shorter, until the chromosomes start unravelling and mistakes are made in cell division. Over time, these mistakes accumulate and contribute to the aging of our various tissues and organs.

Based on our graph mapping lifespan, we were able to make some predictions. If the patterns we found in response to diet resulted from differences in the underlying biology of aging, then a map of the length of telomeres should have the same basic shape as that for mouse longevity.

And did it? Take a look at the graph on the next page for telomere lengths.

Look familiar? If you compare it to the graph for lifespan (above), you can see how closely they match. Low-protein, high-

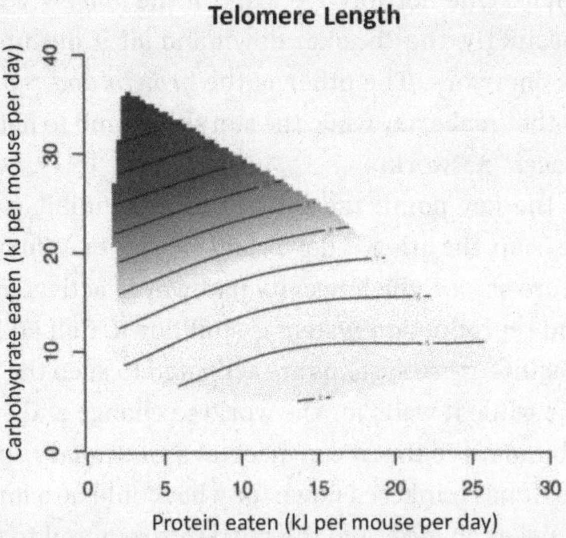

Length of telomeres (in kilo base pairs) in liver cells from mice fed diets differing in protein and carbs. Data from PhD student Rahul Gokarn.

carb mice had longer telomeres and lived longer; high-protein, low-carb mice had shorter telomeres and lifespans. Well and good—that bears out the conventional wisdom where telomeres are concerned (longer is better) as well as our prediction that lower protein coupled with higher carbs equals longer life.

We kept going, measuring macronutrient balance against other markers of aging, such as immune function, activation of key nutrient-signaling pathways, mitochondrial function, and more. They all matched. This meant that we could potentially use diet to turn up or turn down the basic biological mechanisms of aging.

That could be a big deal.

To see why, let's examine these mechanisms of aging in a little more detail.

Sitting at the heart of our physiology (and at that of a mouse or a fly—or even a yeast cell) are two opposing biochemical pathways. Between them, they orchestrate two very different life outcomes in all animals. One network we will call the *longevity pathway*—or less succinctly, the "hunker down and sit it out until things get better" network. The other is the *growth and reproduction pathway*—the "make hay while the sun shines and to hell with the consequences" network.

Here's the key point: these two systems inhibit each other. When one is up, the other is down, and vice versa. When food and nutrients are scarce, the longevity pathway is activated, and the growth and reproduction system is shut down. Cell and DNA repair and maintenance systems are activated to keep the animal in good shape while it waits for the world to change and for food to become abundant so that it can meet its evolutionary objective to reproduce. It has hunkered down for what could be a long wait. If the world never changes and the nutrients required to switch on the growth and reproduction system remain scarce, it will live a long and childless existence.

But when food is abundant and sufficient protein is available, the longevity pathway is shut down and the growth and reproduction one is activated. When this happens, the body starts building new tissues, but at the same time, it turns down the dial on the systems that protect and repair DNA, cells, and tissues from wear and tear. Cells start to make errors when assembling essential proteins, they accumulate misfolded proteins and other cellular garbage, and mistakes increase in frequency during cell division. These problems are an inevitable consequence of living and growing—you can't avoid them any more than you can avoid breathing. As a result, the risk of cancer and other diseases rises, potentially shortening the animal's lifespan. But in evolutionary terms, that's an acceptable price to pay as long as the animal can grow and reproduce.

What we had discovered in our mouse study for the first time was that a low-protein, high-carb diet could switch on the longevity pathway.

Which brings us back to calorie restriction from the previous chapter. We had now shown in flies and mice that the reason 40 percent calorie restriction extends life is not because of the number of calories eaten: macronutrient balance matters more and can act without having to restrict calorie intake. However, in our studies on flies and mice, we gave the animals unlimited access to food. They could eat whenever they wanted and as much as they liked, but only of the particular food each was assigned. This was a different style of experiment from the conventional calorie restriction study on mice, in which the animal is given its reduced allocation of food all in one go, which it promptly eats entirely within an hour or two and sits with nothing until the next day. Under those circumstances, as has now been found by several research groups around the world, it's the time without calories—*fasting*—that activates the longevity system.

So, it's possible to activate the longevity system in mice either by lowering the ratio of protein to carbs (though not necessarily limiting total calorie intake) or by fasting—or by a combination of both.

We kept looking at the mouse data and found we were able to relate diet not just to the biology of aging but to *many* of the various health outcomes that we had measured—glucose tolerance and insulin levels (indicators of type 2 diabetes in humans), blood pressure, cholesterol, and inflammatory markers. You will note that these are all the same markers we get tested for when we're examined by our physician.

And again, there were clear associations. Look at the graphs on the next page.

See, for example, how glucose clearance time was fastest (which is healthy) and LDL cholesterol (the harmful type) lowest on low-protein, high-carb diets and how the surface shades toward dark gray (i.e., worse for health) as protein increased and carb intake fell.

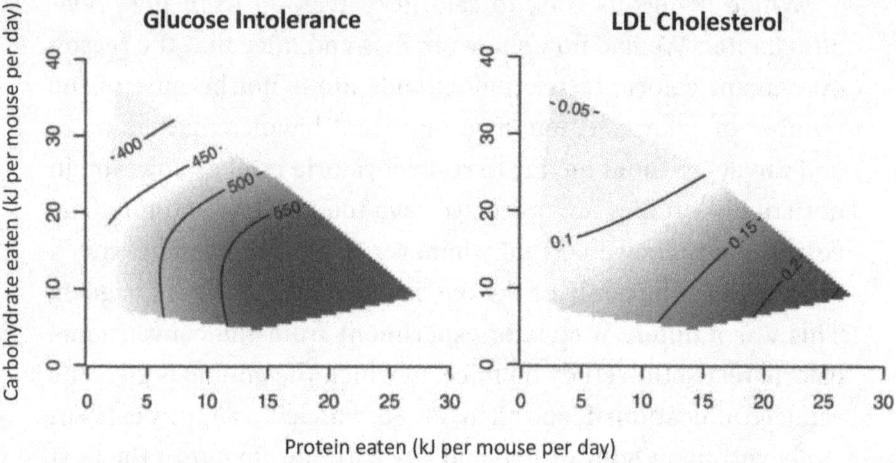

Levels of sugar (AUC) and bad cholesterol (mmol/L) in the blood of mice fed diets differing in protein and carbs. In both cases, lower values (lighter areas, associated with low-protein, high-carb intakes) are healthier than darker regions (associated with high-protein, low-carb intakes).

Not only did the mice who were fed throughout life on a low-protein, high-carb diet live longest, they had the best markers of aging and later-life health. We had learned something which could have fantastic implications for humans who wish to live long and be healthy.

But there was a drawback—and you may have already guessed what that was.

Our low-protein, high-carb mice were fat.

That was because, on the low-protein, high-energy diets, they consumed more total calories than the high-protein mice. This was the effect of protein leverage in mice, as we had been seeing all along: if you live on a diet that's high in fat *or* carbs, you will overeat to get sufficient protein, and you know the rest. As it happens, this response is weaker in mice than in humans but is still enough to cause obesity. Importantly, if we diluted protein moderately with indigestible (and, therefore, zero-calorie) fiber rather than with energy-dense fat or carbs, mice *still* ate more food to get enough protein and lived longer. Only they didn't get fat.

But why would our bodies compel us to eat in ways that made us fat? Surely, obesity is bad for our health, isn't it?

Yes—and no.

When we compared our long-living, healthy but fat mice who ate a low-protein, high-carb diet with equally fat mice on a low-protein, high-fat diet, we saw something significant: the latter group was shorter-lived *and* pretty unhealthy. It meant we could design relatively benign or unhealthy body fatness just by changing the levels of carbs relative to fat. In both cases, mice overate to get more protein, but consuming more fat caused worse health outcomes than eating more carbs (at least the type of carbs used in the experiment, mainly starch).

And so, now the new question was this: What is the difference between benign and unhealthy obesity? Working with colleague Andrew Holmes at the Charles Perkins Centre, we found clues in mouse colons. Low-protein, high-carb mice had a healthier community of microbes living in their gut than did low-protein, high-fat mice. There were differences in other respects, too—including levels of a hormone released from the liver called FGF21, which was strikingly high in the blood of mice on a low-protein, high-carb diet.

FGF21 turns out to be an important signal in the control of protein appetite. It promotes metabolic health by improving sensitivity to insulin, meaning we need to make less insulin to stimulate glucose uptake from the blood into cells. FGF21 also increases energy expenditure under conditions of overeating. Both these factors are important in humans as well as mice. In separate experiments, in collaboration with Chris Morrison at the Pennington Institute in Louisiana, we showed that when levels of FGF21 were increased, mice specifically selected protein-rich foods.

This prompted us to go back to the stored blood samples from the human subjects in our Sydney diet trial (described in Chapter 6), and they, too, had greatly elevated FGF21 levels during the weeks on the 10 percent (low) protein diet. This is fast-moving science—as we write this, several other key papers have just been published confirming that FGF21 is the previously missing protein appetite hormone, as well as being involved in switching off the carb appetite. A huge breakthrough if it holds up.

So, obesity was more complicated than we'd expected, our mice taught us. They showed us that simply being lean does not guarantee a long, healthy life. On the contrary, our sexy, lean mice who ate high-protein, low-carb diets were the shortest-lived of all. They made great-looking middle-aged corpses. This was because the high ratio of protein to carbs was also exactly the mix that supercharges the pathways associated with rapid aging—turning down cell and DNA repair and maintenance mechanisms and promoting aging, cancer, and other chronic diseases.

A bum deal. And, we suspect, not just for mice. After all, when it comes to aging and metabolism, we share the same basic biology with mice—the longevity versus growth and reproduction systems described above are virtually identical in every biochemical detail.

From mice, we learned that we can easily manipulate diet to bring about different outcomes. It's like twisting dials—a little more of this, a little less of that. We can cause obesity (with or without the equivalent of diabetes) or reverse it; or we can prevent diabetes and maximize lifespan; or increase muscle and reduce body fat; prevent or promote cancer; slow or accelerate aging; promote or reduce reproduction; change the gut microbiota; fire up the immune system; on and on. We had done all those things in mice by simply twisting the dials for protein, fats, and carbs. And the results were clearly visualized on graphs, making it easy to recommend very precise diets—for a healthy mouse. But, in principle, for healthy humans, too.

Over the years, we had gained a reputation in the scientific community for running crazily big dietary experiments—first on locusts, then flies, now mice. Sadly, perhaps (but understandably, you'll agree), it's impossible to conduct a similar tightly controlled, birth-to-death test on humans. However, armed with our new understanding gleaned from flies and mice, we turned to the literature on human diet and longevity to see if it contained any useful lessons. Was there any indication there that a low-protein, high-carb diet is associated with long, healthy human lives?

Yes, as it happens. In fact, the longest-lived human populations on the planet all eat exactly such a diet in the so-called Blue Zones popularized by Dan Beuttner in his 2008 book *The Blue Zones: Lessons for Living Longer from the People Who've Lived the Longest.* They also share other non-nutritional features such as good social connectivity and physically active lifestyles. But it is interesting, nonetheless, that based solely on our experiments, the macronutrient balance in their diets would be predicted to extend healthy lifespan.

Perhaps the most famous example of a long-lived Blue Zone population is found on the Japanese island of Okinawa, where centenarians are *five times* more frequent than in the rest of the developed world. The traditional Okinawan diet of principally sweet potato, leafy greens, and low intakes of fish and lean meat contains only 9 percent protein (the lowest found in any human population not suffering food shortages), 85 percent carbs, and just 6 percent fat. This is precisely the same ratio that our mice ate to support maximal lifespan.

Obesity is essentially unknown among traditional Okinawans in part because their diet has high levels of fiber, which is important. With enough fiber in the diet, the power of protein leverage to drive excess calorie intake is limited. Fiber fills up the stomach, slows digestion, and feeds the microbiome—all of which combine to prevent hunger. Much of this fiber is found in the Okinawans' main sources of carbs—sweet potatoes and other vegetables and fruit.

Sadly, today in modern Okinawa, the menu is changing from traditional fare toward the modern Western diet, and obesity and diabetes are on the rise.

Another recently discovered example of an unfeasibly healthy population by modern standards is the Tsimane of Bolivia, who have the lowest recorded incidence of cardiovascular disease in the world. They live a traditional hunter-gatherer existence, augmented with slash-and-burn horticulture. Their diet contains 14 percent protein, 72 percent carbs, and only 14 percent fat. Protein comes mainly from hunted game and river fish. Most of the carbs come from unprocessed rice, plantain, cassava, and corn—like the Okinawans' sweet potatoes, plant-based foods that are high in bulky fiber.

These real-life examples are consistent with the predictions based on our experiments in flies and mice. Which brings us to an important point. Experiments are an indispensable tool for understanding how particular diets influence the health of animals, including our own species. But that is only part of the story. The other part, equally as essential as the first, is knowing which diets animals are *actually* confronted with in their real lives outside of the laboratory and how they respond to the diets that nature offers.

To examine that, we need to hang up our lab coats and head into the wild. Only then can we begin to understand something fundamental about our own dietary dilemma: how we might end up in a mess when we stray far from the nutritional world in which our biology evolved.

CHAPTER 8 AT A GLANCE

1. We embarked upon a huge study on mice, which tested dietary mixtures of protein, carbs, fat, and fiber across the life course.
2. Like flies, mice lived longest and had best mid- to late-life health on low-protein, high-carb diets but had best reproductive potential on higher-protein, lower-carb diets.
3. Low-protein diets extended lifespan by switching on the longevity pathway that protects DNA, cells, and tissues from the inevitable damage done during growth and reproduction. The longevity pathway is universal—from yeast cells to humans.
4. By twisting the dials for protein, fats, carbs, and fiber, we could prevent or cause obesity with or without insulin resistance; extend or shorten lifespan; promote or retard reproduction; increase or decrease muscle mass; change the gut microbiome and immune system; and much more. We had discovered a new way to tailor diet to achieve many ends.

9

Food Environments

NOBEL PRIZE–WINNING PHYSICIST LEON LEDERman observed: “During an intense period of lab work the outside world vanishes and the obsession is total.” This is exactly what we had experienced in the work described to this point on locusts, cockroaches, flies, mice, and other creatures, which helped us uncover some basic truths about obesity and lifespan.

But for us biologists, there is an important difference: a part of the outside world that should never be far from mind is that in which the study species evolved and normally lives. It is those environments that hold the key to understanding *why* the biology we observe in the lab exists as it does, what its significance is for the animal, and what can go wrong when the ancient links between biology and environment are broken by human interference.

Such questions had taken David to the Arizona desert in 1989, two years before we sat together in Steve's office to analyze the data from the big locust experiment. He had come to examine the behavior of a peculiar species of insect in its natural desert environment.

It was getting hot, and I [David] was in trouble of my own making.

I had spent the morning, and several days before that, stalking a grasshopper. This was delicate work: if I got too close, I might spook it, but if too far away, I could lose it. So my attention was fully absorbed—except that I was also keeping guard for rattlesnakes, tarantulas, scorpions, and other hazards in that parched landscape.

Several hours in, and my focus started to drift. The heat was becoming intense, my lips were chapped, and my nostrils and throat were coated with dust. I was getting thirsty.

And then I realized that I had left my backpack, containing water and food, beneath a bush where I first found the animal that morning shortly before sunrise. The choice was stark. If I returned to get the bag, I would lose my prey; if I stayed with it, I would not drink or eat.

I stayed with it.

To understand how I got into this mess and why I didn't make the sensible choice and collect my food and water, we need to consider some of the reasons that Steve and I have formed such a lasting collaborative relationship. We each brought to the partnership a different set of skills and experience, but we also shared much in common in the way we understood biology and nutrition.

One thing we shared is that we had independently come to understand something that, on many occasions, we wished weren't true. We both realized that, as impressive as modern scientific equipment and methods had become, there are some things about animals that can only be learned the hard way: by directly watching them and recording their behavior for hours, even days, on end.

At the time, we were confronted with this inconvenient truth in lab experiments to understand feeding by locusts. In a typical experiment of the sort described in Chapter 1, there would be about forty locusts, each in its own little translucent plastic box containing only the essentials: food, water, and perch on which to rest between meals. A timer was programmed to beep every sixty seconds, signaling that it was time to record what the first, second, third—up to the fortieth—locust was doing, typically leaving about ten seconds for whoever was on shift to "rest" before the next scan began. The cycle was repeated minute after minute, hour after hour, for twelve hours or more, sometimes around the clock and for several days. It was grueling work, involving marathon shifts broken only by kind partners, friends, and colleagues covering for brief periods so we could see to our own biology.

Our results had shown that locust feeding is strikingly regular. The insects would eat, drink, and rest in patterned cycles, a bit like our daily rounds of breakfast, lunch, and dinner. The exact details of the pattern, though, depended on the circumstances, including what type of foods they were eating—and often predictably so.

But there was a problem. As many of our colleagues were quick to remind us, perhaps all that these experiments proved is that, in an artificially regular lab environment, insect behavior is . . . artificially regular. And there was at least a chance that in the wild, something altogether different took place. To find out, we needed to get out of the lab to see if feeding was also regular in the vastly more complex natural food environments where the animals lived and had evolved.

The "food environment" is an important concept and one that will form the main theme of the remaining chapters. It refers to all the factors within an environment that influence nutrition:

the nature, variety, quantity, and availability of foods, as well as the factors that influence an animal's ability to eat available foods. For animals in the wild, these factors might include the risk of being eaten by predators, competition from other animals, and even nonbiological issues like the temperature.

Our challenge was to find a species of grasshopper that could be followed closely enough in the wild to make detailed records of behavior over long, uninterrupted periods comparable to our herculean experiments in the artificial food environments we created in the lab. This is not easy. One issue is that grasshoppers are small and mostly well camouflaged against their botanical backgrounds—they have evolved *not* to be seen, let alone tracked at close range by a gigantic primate several thousand times their size. Another is that the response of grasshoppers to a threat is either to freeze motionless or flee, jumping and flying away. A third challenge is to recognize the individual being followed. Even if we could keep sight of the subject, and it neither froze nor fled, how would we identify it if, no matter how fleetingly, it went out of sight in the presence of other grasshoppers in the group? The prospects weren't looking good.

Then an almost custom-made opportunity arose. Via our colleague Liz Bernays, who was a professor at the University of Arizona in Tucson, we learned of a bug called *Taeniopodo eques*, commonly known as the "horse lubber." The word *lubber* was a promising start. Usually, it refers to a big, clumsy, awkward person—the furthest thing from small, timid, camouflaged grasshoppers feeding in the wild. And horse lubbers live up to their name. Not only are they among the largest, slowest, and boldest grasshoppers, they sport a conspicuous color scheme of bright yellow markings set against a black background. And the males seldom fly, the females not at all.

Here was an animal that had evolved *to be seen*, not to hide, and it had all the swagger and confidence of the invulnerable. And with good reason, courtesy of a toxic cocktail of chemicals they store in their bodies. The bright coloration and confident movement evolved to send the message "Don't mess with me," a combination known as *aposematism,* which is often found in toxic creatures. Horse lubbers even have a backup plan should they encounter a persistent or naïve predator that can't take no for an answer. They lift their wings to expose bright red undersides, a final warning before they discharge their toxic load of vile-smelling froth from their spiracles, a row of portholes along their sides through which they also breathe.

I packed my bags and headed for the Arizona desert.

When I first spent time with the horse lubbers, I did so without recording any data: just watching, getting to know my study animals and the challenges that the desert would throw at me. I soon realized, perfect as the lubbers were for our purposes, they were one step away from *the* perfect grasshopper. What they lacked were nametags, so that I wouldn't confuse one I was tracking with its colleagues.

I overcame this problem by capitalizing on yet another peculiarity in lubber biology. In the evening, when their day's feeding was done, they would climb to about shoulder height on a bush and position themselves for the night ahead. Shortly after sundown, as the last heat of the desert day dissipated, they became too cold to move, fixed like a fridge magnet to the roost. I could then pluck one from its perch, dab it with a code using colored paint markers, and return it as if nothing had happened. Invariably, when I arrived before sunrise the following morning, the animal was exactly as I had left it, ready to track once it had warmed enough in the rising sun to descend and begin the feeding day.

It takes a degree of single-mindedness to wander through a desert for twelve unbroken hours, alone, following an individual grasshopper to note and record its every movement, at the same time collecting samples of each plant on which it fed for later identification. What's more, this was an all-or-none game. I needed a record of the full day's feeding for each grasshopper if we were to match our laboratory experiments. Each success would provide a never-seen window into the secret world of wild grasshoppers. Anything less than a complete day's observation was just wasted hours enduring scorching heat while avoiding the hazards of the desert.

All of this should make it easier to understand why I had followed the grasshopper—which I had named Two-dot Red after the marking scheme I had painted on her back—into the hot desert rather than return to collect my food and water. I was prepared to go thirsty and hungry to avoid losing the lubber.

In all, I collected twelve full-day records of feeding insects, a challenge that required me to travel from Oxford to Arizona during two consecutive years. It was worth it. It helped link all the work we were doing in the lab with what animals do in their natural food environments. Here's how.

Analysis of the results showed that the pattern of feeding in the wild—in the natural food systems where the lubbers evolved—was highly regular, just as we had observed for locusts in simplified food systems in our lab experiments. Also, exactly as we had seen in the lab, the precise details of the feeding pattern changed in response to the food environment.

One example of this regards the role of intense sunlight. On some days that I followed grasshoppers, it was sunny and hot, and on others overcast. On sunny days, without exception, at about noon the lubbers would climb a tree and rest in the shade for several hours until it cooled, usually around three in the afternoon, then continue feeding. When it was overcast, however, the lubbers did not rest but continued to feed throughout the day.

When I looked in detail at *how* the sunlight had influenced lubber feeding, a pattern emerged. Even though the insects had more time for feeding on overcast days, because they weren't forced to shelter from the sun, the amount of time spent feeding was the same as on sunny days. The time saved on cooler, overcast days was spent walking farther, being pickier about which foods they ate, and eating a larger *variety* of foods than on sunny days.

Why might lubbers and other animals be picky when eating in the wild? At the time, many scientists believed the main reason was to avoid overdosing on the various toxic chemicals that plants produce to protect themselves from predators. Our work in the lab suggested another likely answer: animals were trying to eat a diet that provided a balanced nutrient intake. It wasn't until several years later that opportunities arose to test this idea.

This test didn't involve insects . . . but monkeys.

In September 2007, I was on sabbatical leave visiting Steve in Sydney. It was the same time that we were analyzing the data from Kwang's fly experiment (Chapter 7). A PhD student at the Australian National University in Canberra, Annika Felton, contacted us.

Annika had been in the jungles of Bolivia, doing research for her PhD thesis. She had collected feeding data for endangered spider monkeys and wanted to know whether we would like to help with the analysis and interpretation of the vast quantities of feeding and food chemical data she had painstakingly collected. We were immediately interested. Primates would be a wonderful group to test for nutrient regulation in the wild.

We had already shown in lab studies that one species of primate—our own—*does* regulate nutrient intake, with especially strong requirements for protein. As discussed in Chapter 6, this is the biology underlying protein leverage, a discovery that we believed might have important implications for human health. We were interested in knowing more about the origin and function of this characteristic: Which other primates have it, why did it evolve, and can knowing this help in primate conservation?

We also knew that primates offer better opportunities than most animals for collecting the sort of data needed to test for nutrient regulation in undisturbed natural food systems. Unlike most other wild animals, primates can learn to ignore a nonthreatening human observer. This process, called *habituation*, enables skilled observers to approach very close to their study subjects and record behavior in similar detail to our lab studies of insects.

Annika had done an excellent job. She followed individual monkeys from dawn to dusk, recording everything they ate, in much the same way as I had followed lubbers in the Arizona desert. But she also recorded *how much* of each food was eaten in each meal—for example, ten small and five medium-size ripe figs of species X, plus six small and four large leaves of species Y—and collected samples of each to take to the lab for chemical analysis. She had done exactly what was needed to test for nutrient regulation in a wild primate. And yet, as we later came to learn, Annika had ridden a roller coaster of highs and lows to get to the point where she had the data to share.

In 2003, Annika and her partner, Adam, who are passionately committed to conserving the earth's forests, traveled to Bolivia as volunteers for the Wildlife Conservation Society. On their expedition, in the Madidi National Park in the Amazon river basin in northwestern Bolivia, the team discovered a new species of monkey. That's a notable event and one that few people will ever experience. On the other hand, if it were going to happen anywhere, Madidi is the place; it's a part of the largest stretch of conserved land in the world and among the most biologically diverse. Which is why what happened next is all the more remarkable.

The naming of newly discovered species is an interesting business. Occasionally, scientists name new species they discover after themselves. More commonly, the name is chosen to reflect some distinctive feature of the animal or its habitat. This is the case for the house fly, *Musca domestica*—*Musca* indicates the group of flies to which it belongs and *domestica* its habit of plaguing our houses. Other species are named to honor famous people. For example, in 2009, scientists at the Western Australian Museum named sixteen new species, eleven of which had the second name *darwinii,* and a jellyfish, *Phiallela zappa,* is named after Frank Zappa. In 2005, beetles that gorge on slime molds growing on fungus were named after George W. Bush, Dick Cheney, and Donald Rumsfeld. (The scientists were politically conservative, and it was meant as an honor!)

Annika and the team, led by Dr. Bob Wallace, took a different approach. They decided to auction the naming rights for the new species. It was ultimately to be called *Plecturocebus aureipalatii*, the second name meaning "golden palace," after an online casino of the same name. This is fitting, considering a characteristic feature of the monkey is its distinct golden crown. The casino paid $650,000 for the privilege. The entire sum was donated to help maintain the home of the golden palace monkey, Madidi National Park.

Annika developed a passion for studying primates, and this was not because they are charismatic, intelligent relatives of our own species or because selling naming rights can be profitable. Rather, she wanted to understand the complex and important roles that monkeys play in the ecological economy of the forests and how monkeys contribute to maintaining the forests that sustain them. As you might imagine, this information could be important for conservation.

For her study, Annika selected a troop of endangered spider monkeys in the La Chonta forestry concession in Bolivia. The region she selected was undisturbed, but being a forestry concession, could be logged in the future. It was therefore very important to know which species of trees the primate relied on and why. Only in this way, Annika knew, could the forests be logged sustainably to conserve the monkeys.

To say that the regions Annika chose for her study were undisturbed is an understatement. There were no tracks, no paths, no camp, not even a map of the area. Her first job, assisted by a knowledgeable local and three volunteers, was to find a troop of monkeys. Next, they built a basecamp and cut a network of trails through the forest along which to move in their studies.

When the team first discovered the monkeys, a large troop of about fifty, there was no welcoming reception. They had seldom seen humans, if at all, and were in no mood for change. Outraged, they hurled sticks, aggressively waved branches, and screamed. But the team persisted, for six months gently and unobtrusively maintaining a presence as close as the troop would allow.

The patience paid off. Gradually, young monkeys began to climb down the trees to take a curious look at the strange but now familiar visitors. The stick-throwing, branch-waving, and shouting slowed at first, then stopped. Annika and her team could finally get close enough to record feeding as if at the same dining table.

Then disaster struck. First, Annika got dengue fever, a nasty disease caused by a virus carried by mosquitoes. Intense headaches, muscle and joint pain, extreme fatigue, vomiting, diarrhea, rashes, and bleeding gums are among the symptoms. Dengue is bad enough in the safety of civilization but truly terrible in a remote forest not even known to maps. Not long after Annika had recovered, nature once again flexed its muscle. A huge storm tore through the jungle, destroying the camp, including the team's precious water containers. There was no option but to start from scratch, now also building a dam to replace the lost water tanks.

With dengue fever and violent storms still fresh in mind, a third disaster struck: this time a ferocious forest fire. Reluctant to rebuild again, Annika dug in, urgently clearing all flammable bushes from around the camp before they caught fire. In most circumstances, this would be a challenge. But Annika had for some time been suffering headaches, which she assumed was a lingering symptom of dengue fever or from the relentless hours staring up at monkeys in the trees. Now she also started feeling nauseous—no doubt the result of breathing the thick palls of smoke that smothered the camp. Eventually, she could hold no longer and radioed for help. It arrived just in time: the vehicle shuddered down the primitive road with flames lapping at both sides.

Although it didn't seem very lucky at the time, this third crisis was as close as any to Victorian poet Elizabeth Barrett Browning's observation that "the luck of the third adventure is proverbial." The team traveled to the nearest major city, Santa Cruz, to regroup while the forest burned. Usually, after long periods in inhospitable environments like the Bolivian jungles, there is a childlike delight in returning to civilization—seeing new people, eating different foods, and appreciating the basic comforts we take for granted, like electricity and running water.

Not so for Annika. Her headaches continued, and her nausea lingered. She decided to get checked. What she found has made her ever grateful to the fire that chased her from the jungle to the comforting reach of medical science. An MRI scan showed a tumor the size of a walnut growing like a deadly parasite in her brain. Three days later, she was back in Australia preparing for surgery (which is just as well; she was successfully treated and has resumed her career as a researcher).

Between first arriving at the field site and fleeing the flames, fifteen months had passed. In that time, she had not only endured a litany of challenges but also managed to collect thirty-eight full-day records of monkeys feeding. When, in 2007, we sat together in Sydney looking at the data, we had no idea of the travails she had endured to collect them, but we immediately saw their value.

To understand Annika's results, we need to consider what the monkeys eat. Their diet consists of several types of foods, including ripe fruit, immature fruit, flowers, young leaves and old leaves, all from various species. Of all these foods, they have a special liking for the ripe fruits of one kind of fig whenever it is available.

Annika naturally wondered why they liked this fig so much, so she looked closely at its composition. One possibility was that it had high concentrations of some nutrient that was lacking in the monkeys' food environment—just as we saw that Mormon crickets eat each other to gain precious protein. For these primates, though, it was unlikely that protein would be the scarce nutrient, because it was all over the forests where they live: young leaves contain it in abundance, and there is no shortage of those in tropical forests. It seemed that fats and carbs were more likely to drive the monkeys' fig infatuation. And yet, their fig was not particularly high in fats and carbs compared to some other fruits that excited the monkeys less.

Then Annika noticed something interesting. On the many days when the favored figs were not available, the monkeys consumed lots of different foods, none of which alone had the same composition as the figs; but together, they always added up to—almost exactly—the same mixture of proteins, fats, and carbs found in their favorite fruit.

The conclusion seemed inescapable: the monkeys liked those particular figs because they contained the optimal balance of macronutrients. When the figs weren't available, the monkeys somehow knew which combinations of other foods they should eat to compose a balanced diet. This and many studies since involving other primate species leave no doubt that nutrient balancing is not confined to laboratory studies; primates in the wild do the same. Annika's discovery could also have important practical benefits. The fig in question, called *Ficus boliviana,* is a favorite not only of the monkeys but also of the logging industry. The new information could help the Bolivian authorities realize the importance of conserving these trees.

One more question—the question we were most excited about—needed to be examined in Annika's data: *How do the monkeys respond when neither their favorite figs nor suitable combinations of other foods are available for them to select a diet with their preferred macronutrient balance?* In equivalent circumstances, we already knew, humans would eat until they got their fill of protein, whether this involved overeating fats and carbs (on low-protein diets) or undereating them (on high-protein diets) (Chapter 6). Was this the same for monkeys in the wild?

The result was unmistakable: spider monkeys did exactly what we had seen in the lab for many other species, including humans. They maintained a constant intake of protein, allowing fat and carb intake to vary with dietary macronutrient balance. This was exciting. It provided the first example of a nonhuman primate showing the same pattern of nutrient regulation as our own species—the protein prioritization pattern.

Pretty significant, given that this was the first demonstration of the humanlike pattern of nutrient regulation for any animal in the wild. But it didn't mean that the ability to balance a diet in this way was shared by all or even a few other primates, or by any other species.

Which is a good point at which to move to the forests of Uganda, where I was with friend and colleague Jessica Rothman, an expert in primate nutritional ecology, examining data for mountain gorillas. In four months of the year, both carb-rich fruits and protein-rich leaves are available, enabling the gorillas to select their preferred dietary balance of 19 percent protein. In the remaining eight months, fruits are extremely scarce, and they are forced onto an all-leaf diet containing 31 percent protein—higher than almost any other herbivore and equivalent to what dogs eat (Chapter 5).

If these gorillas were like humans and spider monkeys, during those eight months without fruit they would have continued to eat the target amount of protein and, as a result, much less fats and carbs than during the fruit months.

And yet they didn't. They overate protein to ensure they ate the same amount of energy-rich fats and carbs. This was a fascinating result. We now knew that different primates differed in their responses to variation in dietary balance in the wild—spider monkeys were like humans, and gorillas were not.

Why are gorillas so different in this respect? A likely answer is suggested by our studies on insects and other animals in the lab. We had noticed that the only species to respond like the gorillas did were all predators. What gorillas have in common with predators is that both have a very high-protein diet. Predators eat meat, and for eight months of the year, mountain gorillas eat leaves so high in protein that their diet has twice the percentage of nutrient (31 percent) as is typical for humans (around 15 percent) and three times that of spider monkeys (around 10 percent).

With diets so high in protein, predators and gorillas face the same challenge: getting enough fats and carbs to fuel their energy needs. Failing to do so, as we saw in Chapter 7, can lead to serious problems, including population declines. No wonder, then, that both groups regulate their macronutrient intake in the way they do, with the biggest priority being to hit the target amount of fats and carbs even if this involves overeating protein.

An important message was emerging from the comparison of humans, spider monkeys, and gorillas: appetites can evolve differently even within a single group of animals—in this case primates—depending on the food environment. An opportunity to add another piece of information to the puzzle—and a lot more besides—arose in 2012, when Jessica and I were invited to present papers at the American Association of Physical Anthropologists conference in Portland, Oregon.

One reason I was eager to travel the long distance from New Zealand, where I was based, to Portland is that Jessica had arranged for me to meet her friend and colleague Erin Vogel. We planned to discuss collaborating on a project to understand nutrient selection in Erin's study animals: wild orangutans in Borneo.

By then, Erin had already collected large amounts of data, consisting of thousands of hours' worth of observations of almost fifty orangutans, assembled over several years, and data collection was continuing daily. Perhaps here was a perfect opportunity to understand further the role of protein in natural food environments.

Borneo was hard going. The team would leave camp at around 4 a.m. and head into the pitch-dark forest. In places, the ground was so swampy that the only reasonable way to move was on custom-built boardwalks. Shortly before we arrived, a large king cobra was seen moving over the first boardwalk along the route into the forest. On another occasion, the research team met a clouded leopard on the same boardwalk.

Mostly, we knew exactly where we were heading as we followed the narrow beams of our headlamps. This was because the orangutan we were tracking usually had also been followed the day before, and when it stopped feeding and built a nest in which to sleep for the night, we marked the exact location using a GPS.

The following morning, we would arrive at the nest while it was still dark, in much the same way I did when studying lubbers in Arizona. Careful not to wake the ape sleeping in the tree above, we would then string portable hammocks above the swampy ground between selected trees and lie quietly in the dark until the orangutan awoke. These were precious moments: hearing the forest awake exactly as it had for hundreds of thousands of years, as the black treetops slowly turned to gray, then green, often in softly dripping rain.

At some point, when we heard movement in the tree above, typically accompanied by a deluge of drops shaken off the moist leaves, we knew the day's work had begun. But there was no telling what would happen. Sometimes long periods would pass in which *nothing* happened—the orangutan neither fed nor moved elsewhere. We took these opportunities to rest in our hammocks, waiting. At other times, the ape would feed, and it took our full concentration to record its actions. Then, at some point, it would decide to move on, usually headed for an alternative food source.

That required immediate action. We quickly rolled our hammocks, repacked our backpacks, and followed. Experts at moving through the treetops, orangutans have no respect for boardwalks or trails, and so following on the ground was heavy going.

One day I was out in the field with Shauhin Alavi, a PhD student under Erin's supervision. Shauhin competes in kickboxing contests when not chasing apes in the swamp forests. No slouch then, but together we would encounter an orangutan that would test us both.

At first, it was just another day in the office. Our chosen animal, Juni, awoke, ate some breakfast, and then hung around, moving a bit, then nibbling again, then moving, never over long distances. This went on for several hours. Eventually, the waiting made me hungry, so I unpacked my lunch. As I started to eat, the orangutan took off, seemingly with a purpose. Food and hammocks hastily repacked, we followed, stopping a while later beneath the tree in which Juni had once again settled. Just as it seemed we had once again entered a long wait and I had unpacked my lunch, off she went again. This pattern repeated itself several frustrating times. Then things got worse.

At about 2:30 in the afternoon, she took off and this time didn't stop. Already beyond the boardwalks, we were now dragged off the trails, across swamps, over fallen trees, and through dense thickets with razor-sharp leaves and thorns. Several times, I stepped into mud nearly to the knee, having first to remove my foot from my boot to get free, then excavate the boot from the swamp.

More than two hours later, Juni eventually stopped and again started shuffling around the same location. With hands cut, arms scratched, and socks plastered in mud, now the heavy rain was penetrating my waterproofing to my skin. At least now it was time for her to settle and build a nest for the night, allowing us to return to camp, check for leeches, get dry, eat dinner, and prepare for the following day in the forest.

We weren't so lucky. She continued to dither about, looking as though she were about to build a nest, then starting one and abandoning it, and then beginning another elsewhere. When she eventually settled, the forest was nearly as dark as it had been when we entered it, which by now seemed like several days earlier. It was as if she wanted to send one last message about the challenges of stalking orangutans through swamp forests in Borneo. The message was received, loud and clear.

This was all worthwhile. When we converted the observations into nutrient intakes and looked at these in a geometric plot, the seemingly haphazard eating—now leaves, now fruit, stopping and then moving—all made perfect sense, especially when we combined them with the bigger dataset that Erin had collected over several consecutive years, involving dozens of orangutans.

Regardless of what we saw on any given day—how much leaves and fruit were eaten, how far the orangutans moved or where—one thing was always the same: on each day they ate the same amount of protein. What differed widely across days, weeks, months, and years was the amount of fats and carbs eaten. But even this difference was highly consistent: when the diet was rich in fruits and therefore had a low concentration of protein, fat and carb intake was high; and when the diet was low in fruits but rich in leaves, fat and carb intake was low.

We were seeing, in an ape, the same protein-centered behavior we strongly suspect underlies the obesity epidemic in humans. Can the orangutans help us understand more about our own species? To answer this, we needed to know whether the intake of fats and carbs by orangutans has anything to do with obesity. Do they store it as fat, or does it pass straight through them? And if they do store it, *why* do they do this?

As you may realize by now, research—especially in the wild—is filled with challenges. Measuring the body weight or fat content of wild orangutans, without disturbing them, is no exception. And yet primatologists have a very clever way of doing so. Here's how it's done.

The observer is equipped with a special scientific instrument, which, unlike most others, was invented not by engineers but by field biologists themselves. The instrument consists of a long, forked stick with a clean plastic bag tethered between the short y-arms at the far end. During observations, the animal will occasionally pause its activities, go still, and then release a torrent of clear golden pee from its perch in the tree above. Rapid reactions are needed, and caution must be exercised. But with experience, a sample of fresh urine—which has touched nothing but pure air since leaving the animal—can be collected in the bag. Immediately transferred to small sterile plastic containers, the urine is later analyzed in the lab for key chemicals that are released in different concentrations when the animal is in different physiological states.

One chemical, called *C-peptide*, provides a marker of how open the cells are to absorbing glucose from the blood and storing it as fat. In medicine, this marker is used to assess the function of the cells in the pancreas that manufacture insulin, the hormone that causes fat cells to take up glucose from the blood. A second group of chemicals, called *ketones*, tell us the opposite: they provide a measure of how much fat is being drawn from storage to burn for energy. In humans, ketones increase during starvation and on weight-loss diets that are so low in carbohydrates that the body turns to burning body fat.

Our chemical informants tell a fascinating story. When fruits are abundant, providing an energy-rich diet, C-peptide levels are high and ketones low in the urine—the orangutans store the abundant carbs as body fat. Ketones, on the other hand, reach high levels when fruits are scarce and the diet consists of protein-rich leaves—meaning that in these periods, they use their fat stores for energy. This shows that, as in humans, variation in energy intake does, indeed, relate to body fat in orangutans.

This pattern makes perfect sense in light of orangutan ecology. In the forests of Borneo, fruit availability is unpredictable. Sometimes it is superabundant and sometimes scarce. The orangutans' strategy for dealing with this uncertainty is to grab fats and carbs when they are available and live off body fat when they are scarce. All the while, they use the ever-abundant leaves to ensure that their protein needs are met.

From the lubbers of the Arizona desert, to spider monkeys, gorillas, and orangutans, the challenges and excitement of studying foraging in natural food environments were paying off. It told us, first, that the kinds of nutrient regulation we had established under simple and highly regular conditions in lab studies also played a very important role in foraging in the wild.

It also showed that, to understand nutrition, we needed to know how appetites engaged with the food environments where animals live. Hot midday temperatures reduced the variety of foods eaten by lubbers but not the amount; mountain gorillas living in forests where fruits are scarce overeat protein to get enough energy from fats and carbs; and spider monkeys and orangutans maintain a constant protein intake, allowing fats and carbs to vary with fruit availability—as do we.

How can these insights help understand and improve nutrition in our own species? This is the question we address in the following three chapters.

CHAPTER 9 AT A GLANCE

1. The term *food environment* refers to the factors within an environment that influence diet and nutrition—the kinds and amounts of foods available and the things that influence the animal's consumption of those foods.
2. Studying animals in their natural food environments is important for understanding what roles the characteristics we observe in lab studies, such as strong protein appetites, play in their normal lives.
3. In their natural food environments, our wild primate cousins select food combinations that provide a nutritionally balanced diet. When natural fluctuations in food availability prevent them from doing so, they have specially evolved responses to cope with dietary imbalance.
4. Orangutans are adapted to natural fluctuations in the availability of carb- and fat-rich fruits in their forest habitat. Regardless of fruit availability, their strong protein appetite ensures they get neither too much nor too little of that nutrient. When fruits are abundant, they eat them in large amounts and store the energy as body fat to get them through periods when fruits are scarce.
5. What happens when food environments to which animals are adapted change permanently?

10

Changing Food Environments

It was an unusual working day in September 2018, even for a field biologist. Exhilarated and euphoric from physical exertion, I gazed in awe at the vast, pristine landscape. The air was thin and crisp and the light an almost artificially pure silver gilded in thin golden sunrays.

I had walked four days through the Bhutanese Himalaya, the past two hours up a steep, rocky path through freezing mist, rain, and sleet. Each step was mechanical and deliberate, measured against the meager oxygen my lungs could extract from the thin air. The only view was a small radius of wet path ahead, rising mountain to the right, and the beginnings of a precipitous drop on the left, cocooned in thick mist. Sound was muffled except for the rhythm of deep breathing and crunching shale beneath my mountain boots. Occasionally, it all faded into excited thoughts of reaching the top.

But there was also trepidation about what I might meet there. Several times over previous days, I had looked up at the cascades of mist rolling over mountain passes high above. They were powered by jet streams of wind capable of making rain, sleet, and people horizontal. Sometimes I saw blizzards of snow stripped from the peaks, traveling like scythes in the ferocious winds. With the low visibility and the long distance to cover before nightfall, the thought was never far off that, in these conditions, the situation could quickly turn nasty.

But it didn't. As if scripted, when the gradient eased, then flattened, and the trail tilted downhill for the first time in hours, the sleet stopped, and the fog opened to expose a gently fluttering string of tattered and faded prayer flags set against the vastness. My two Bhutanese colleagues, Lhendup Tharchen and Sonam Dorje, and I were elated. Both expert mountain men, enthusiastic photographers, and experienced naturalists, they explained that views of such clarity from this hostile pass are rare. Our timing was impeccable.

David was here, in Bhutan, for a simple reason. From the previous chapter, it should be clear that food environments are half the story when it comes to determining what creatures eat. The rest is their nutrient appetites and other mechanisms that have evolved to deal with a specific food environment. Could it be that the nutrition crisis our species is confronting is a result of this—our tendency to change our food environment faster than we can adapt? If so, perhaps the lessons we have learned from other species might help explain why we eat in ways that damage our health.

To test that proposition, we first needed to understand *how* human food environments have changed.

I stood quietly to observe. Ahead and 300 feet below, the ridge transitioned to a rolling plateau, rust-colored with plants withering in the autumn cold, except for a turquoise heart-shaped lake, which soon would freeze. Behind, across a narrow arm of the valley from which we had climbed, were massive scree slopes, glistening mercury silver from the wet, beneath a crest of rocky crags. Elsewhere, snowcapped peaks protruded into the now clear sky like the teeth of some mythical monster.

I had never seen such a landscape; yet, in one respect, it was no different from the Arizona desert, the rain forests of Uganda, the swamp forests of Borneo, and the many other wild places I've worked. Like all the rest, it is a food environment. We had come to understand the challenges facing an unusual primate that lives there: our own species.

To understand why, we need to go back in time millions of years to a period before humans evolved, when all primates resembled the monkeys, gorillas, orangutans, and other nonhuman species that primatologists study today.

One thing we can't help noticing about the diets of these species is how similar they are. Even though spider monkeys, gorillas, and orangutans differ in how they regulate nutrient intake—the monkeys and orangutans prioritize protein, the gorillas don't—the basic diet of all three is the same. It consists mostly of fruits high in carbs and fats and leaves high in protein, just in different proportions and eaten in particular times of the year or in different patterns across years.

This suggests that the diets of these primates have remained essentially similar for millions of years. The last common ancestor shared by spider monkeys, gorillas, and orangutans, approximately forty million years ago, probably ate much the same diet as all three do now, as did most of the more recent ancestors leading to the species we study today.

Is this telling us that primates are inflexible and unable to change their diets? No, many exceptions prove otherwise. Primates that have moved from the tropics to environments where fruits are scarce, such as the temperate forests in Asia, *have* successfully changed their diets. Like their tropical cousins, they still eat leaves, but instead of fruit, they have switched to carb-rich seeds like acorns. Many primates also eat protein-rich animal foods, especially insects. Mostly, the contribution of these to the diet is very low, even miniscule—not because they don't like them, but because insects are so much more difficult to catch in sufficient quantities to supply a primate's protein needs. But there are exceptions; small primates, with lower protein requirements, *can* find enough insects to satisfy their modest needs, and some do exactly that.

There are also examples where primates have changed their diets not through long periods of evolution, as in the shift from tropical to temperate forests or changes in body size, but very rapidly. One is the baboons of Masai Mara National Reserve, which switched from their normal diet to eating the kitchen scraps from a tourist resort. Another is the green vervet monkey of the Caribbean island of St. Kitts. These monkeys are not native to the island but were introduced there in the 1600s with the slave trade. Some of the monkeys escaped to the wild and quickly discovered the abundant, juicy mangoes in that tropical paradise. Before long, they got what surely seemed luckier still: they learned that the bamboo-like crops growing on the island were filled with pure sugar. Then their dietary flexibility went a step further. Nobody knows exactly how it happened, but somehow they developed a fondness for the product that was made from the St. Kitts sugar cane: rum.

Clearly, the diets of primates *are* flexible and can quickly adjust to new opportunities. So why then have many remained so constant over millions of years? The reason is the animals seldom encounter new opportunities—their environments have remained essentially the same or have changed only very slowly over long periods.

To us, it might sound boring, even tedious, living in similar circumstances year in and year out—where's the progress in that? But it has an important benefit. It enables the biology of primates to adapt superbly to their food environments—much like the orangutans have adapted to surviving long periods without fruits. The downside, though, is that when change does occur, the adapted biology might not know how to cope. Once the resort opened nearby, the Masai Mara baboons became fat on a human diet and developed diabetes and several other health issues, including high cholesterol. The St. Kitts vervet monkeys are now alcoholics, taken to stealing drinks from tourists when their backs are turned.

And that brings us to our own species. At some point, around three million years ago, a primate evolved that was quite different from any that had come before—the first-ever human species or, technically, member of the genus *Homo*. The details are scant, but what seems certain is that changes in climate and their effects on the African environment played an overriding role. The climate had become cooler, drier, and more variable. These changes affected the habitat of our distant ancestor not only directly but indirectly via its effects on other species, including the foods they ate. Climate had driven changes in the food environment, and evolution was responding.

At first, the rapid environmental change took its toll. Several human species evolved; exactly how many is not known. But what *is* known is that almost all of these species—in fact all but one—went extinct. The rate of change outstripped their capacity to adapt.

The surviving lineage bucked the trend and coped with the changing environments by mastering a very neat trick. They found that the best way to deal with rapidly changing environments was through changing them even more rapidly. They learned, so to speak, to fight fire with fire.

This might even be literally true. Exactly what was different about our ancestors is hard to tell, and probably there is no one thing—it was a combination of interrelated changes. But anthropologists agree two factors played lead roles: the control of fire and the manufacture of stone tools.

Stone tools are not unique to humans; they are also used by other primate species. Bearded capuchin monkeys in Brazil use stones to crack open the hard shells of nuts. They do this in a very sophisticated way, placing the nut on a stone anvil and bashing it with a carefully selected hammer-like rock. There is, though, no other species that has used fire.

Both stone tools and fire were, foremost, technologies meant to control the food environment. I am collaborating with Patricia Izar, based at the University of São Paulo, to examine why bearded capuchin monkeys go to all that effort to crack open nuts. The answer, we are finding, is that it's worth the effort, since the nuts provide rich packages of balanced nutrition. Ancestral humans, too, used tools principally for nutrition—for hunting and preparing foods.

Richard Wrangham of Harvard University has done some research showing the importance of cooking for improving the diets of early humans. In his "Cooking Hypothesis," Wrangham argues that the control of fire was *the* key change that made our ancestors human. It changed our diet forever, providing a new food environment to which our biology then adapted.

Whatever the exact cause, one thing is sure: the combination of fire and tools enabled humans to change their food system like no other species in the history of life has ever done. Initially, the change was positive. Our ancestors used their ingenuity to create an environment that was, in terms of diet and nutrition, the original Garden of Eden.

Or, perhaps, we should think of this as *environments*. In this period, the Paleolithic, humans ate diverse, wholesome diets consisting of fiber-rich vegetables, tubers, fruits, and lean, wild meat containing low proportions of saturated fats and higher levels of healthy polyunsaturated ones. Some hunter-gatherer groups are thought to have eaten diets high in protein, with most estimates suggesting that fats and carbs provided 70 percent or less of calories, meaning protein contributed around 30 percent. Compare that with typical modern diets, in which fats and carbs contribute 85 percent or more, and protein just half of what those populations ate in the paleo era. Other hunter-gatherer populations, new studies suggest, ate diets lower in protein and higher in carbohydrates. Regardless of this diversity in protein and carbohydrate, one thing was common in the diets of our pre-agriculture ancestors. They consisted of whole foods, rich in micronutrients and fiber.

Ancient skeletons from this period show that people were tall, lean, muscular, and healthy, and nutritional deficiencies were rare. We should, nonetheless, be careful not to romanticize this period nor attempt to replicate the diet. Average lifespans were short, mostly due to death during childbirth, injuries, and infectious diseases. There is also evidence of deadly violence, including blows to the head from heavy objects and slit throats—the sinister side of tool use. In such a world, where the privilege of dying of old age was enjoyed by few, the life-shortening effect of a high-protein diet was less relevant than it is today. And, as we will discuss later, we are not the same animal as we were then—some of our nutritional needs have changed.

Although nobody knows for sure why, roughly 12,000 years ago, in an area around the border of what today we call Iran and

Iraq, the human food environment began to change again. At first, those involved might not have even noticed that anything important was taking place. On any given day, the vegetation around the camp might have been just a little different, if at all, from the previous month, or even the year or generation before that. Seeds accidentally dropped from plants that were gathered for food began to grow around the camp in higher densities, while other less popular plants became scarcer. Plants previously gathered from farther away were eaten less. The changes accumulated, and within a few generations, something had occurred that was again to transform the human food environment. Dramatically. Forever.

People began to deliberately plant the seeds of edible plants and weed out the rest. They came to rely less on the foods they foraged and more on crops they cultivated. Later, the same was to happen with animals—instead of hunting game, humans tamed and herded wild animal populations, which adapted to this new lifestyle. Plants and animals were becoming domesticated, and our species was transitioning from a lifestyle of hunting and gathering to one based on farming.

The change spread quickly, at first across the Middle East including modern-day Syria, Jordan, Israel, Palestine, and southeastern Turkey, and then through Europe. Over the centuries that followed, similar events took place independently in different regions across the world—Africa, Asia, Papua New Guinea, Australia, and the Americas included. Agriculture was invented several times, independently, by populations across the globe.

Farming was, clearly, a popular lifestyle choice. And yet it's not immediately obvious why. What we do know is that populations increased, principally because of the rise in birthrates, and became more settled compared with their hunter-gatherer histories. Surprisingly, though, daily life was, for the majority, not improved and in many respects worse than before.

Although the details vary, in general, early agricultural societies came to rely heavily on a few staple foods, mostly grains high in carbohydrates and low in micronutrients. Dietary diversity dropped, with more calories coming from carb-rich grains and fewer wild foods. People became shorter, and many skeletons from these periods show signs of nutrient deficiencies and other food-related problems, including tooth decay. There were also cases of degenerative joint disease, suggesting that early farmers lived physically tough lives.

At the same time, the high population densities and close proximity to domesticated animals and pests, such as rats, increased the threat of epidemics of infectious disease, including tuberculosis, syphilis, and the plague. Added to that, the reliance on few crops and domesticated animals made people living in agricultural food environments vulnerable to famine. The risk of starvation was never far off.

But with time, life on the farm improved. Increased structuring of society, better technology, and the diversification of farmed species, including increased production of animal products, reduced the vulnerability of farmers to starvation and improved the healthfulness of their diets. The new food environment had matured, and humans and their plant and animal co-inhabitants had adapted to it.

Adaptation was by two means. First, innovations in cultural knowledge helped to adapt dietary practices and food processing techniques to agricultural food environments. There are many examples, one concerning the origins of dairy farming. Milk contains a rather peculiar sugar, lactose, which is found nowhere else in the animal kingdom. Lactose cannot be absorbed from the gut directly, and infant mammals first need to digest it into smaller sugars that can be absorbed, using an enzyme called lactase. Typically, though, mammals produce lactase only during infancy—meaning that they can no longer drink milk beyond this point without risking unpleasant outcomes such as diarrhea and extreme bloated flatulence.

Early dairy farmers learned to overcome this by various means. One is using bacteria to ferment the lactose into lactic acid, which can be absorbed through the gut and used for nutrition. The benefits are obvious: fermenting milk provided a rich source of animal-derived nutrients that could be obtained without killing the producer. To this day, many of the dairy products we eat are "predigested" by bacteria in this way, including yogurt, some cheeses, and to some extent, sour cream.

Bacterial fermentation and other cultural means were not the only mechanisms through which early farmers made this rich source of food available. Some populations also evolved, through Darwinian natural selection, the ability to produce the digestive enzyme lactase beyond infancy and therefore digest milk directly. This happened at least twice, independently, in the history of agriculture—once in the region around what today we call Hungary and the other in Africa. Even though the outcome of these two evolutionary events is the same—unlike other mammals, these humans can digest milk throughout their lives—different mutations were involved in the two populations.

And this is not the only example of genetic changes that have helped adapt humans and other species to agricultural food environments. Another, which we already mentioned in Chapter 5, is the duplication of genes that produce starch-digesting enzymes—duplication that has better adapted domesticated dogs to living off starchy human table scraps. Rodents (rats and mice) and pigs, other species that eat human food scraps, also have evolved duplicated starch-digesting genes.

These and many other cultural and genetic adaptations ensured that humans became well suited to their newly developed agricultural food environments, just as they had previously been to their Paleolithic hunter-gatherer environments. We were, once again, living in a Garden of Eden—this time of our own making.

Then things began to change—again. And this is what had brought Lhendup, Sonam, and me up that high pass in the Bhutanese Himalaya.

We had come to examine the lifestyles of the Lingzhi people, also referred to as *lagungsum gi mi,* meaning "people of the highlands." The Lingzhi are part of a larger group of seminomadic pastoralists, whose lifestyle can be traced through all the historical stages of human food environments, from hunter-gatherers to successful farming.

Around 30,000 years ago, hunter-gatherers began to move into a vast high-altitude area in central Asia, the Tibetan plateau. Spanning over 15,000 square miles, at an average height of almost 14,000 feet, it is both the largest and the highest plateau on Earth—which is why it is sometimes referred to as "the roof of the world." In their newly adopted habitat, the ancient migrants encountered large herds of wild bison-like creatures, with formidable horns, dense mats of fur dangling to just above the ground, and big furry tails. With males almost 14 feet long, standing to 7 feet at the shoulder, and weighing over 2,000 pounds, these animals would be viewed with extreme care by any sensible person today. Back then, they were viewed as an unprecedented opportunity. Rock art in the region records dramatic scenes with hunters often perilously close to being trampled or gored. These creatures, some of which still live on the Tibetan plateau, are wild yaks.

With time, some individuals, or groups of yaks, became a little less wild than others and began to associate more closely with the bands of humans than the wild herds of their own species. Perhaps they were captured as calves and raised in a human environment, were innately less wild than others, or both. Whatever the cause, in this new environment, where domesticated life offered features that benefited the yaks, evolution took a new course. The yaks gradually changed, and so did the culture of the hunter-gatherers with which they were becoming associated.

By 5,000 years ago, one group of humans, the Qiang people, had become inseparably associated with the changing yaks. The animals provided meat, milk, fur, hide, dung to fuel fires or fertilize gardens, transport, and other forms of labor. They, in turn, were protected from predators, shepherded to the best grazing grounds, and males were provided mating opportunities without first having to survive violent competition with other candidates, as is the case in the wild. The yaks had become fully domesticated, and the Qiang people had transitioned from hunter-gatherers to pastoralists, whose living was dependent on yaks. Among the evolutionary changes that took place during domestication of yaks were a reduction in body size and the development of a more placid temperament. A recent study showed that domesticated yaks differ from their wild ancestors by as many as 209 genes, several of which are associated with tame behavior.

In the centuries that followed, the yak-herding lifestyle spread through high-altitude regions in Asia, including the Himalayas. There, where grazing opportunities are sharply seasonal, the yak herders migrate with their herds in the spring to the lush new vegetation growth at high altitudes, living in tents made of hide, often with dogs to protect the yaks from snow leopards. In the fall, when the summer grazing grounds turn brown and begin to freeze, and the weather becomes too hostile for humans to survive, they return to homes at lower altitudes. So important are yaks to the mountain people that they have been named "the gold of Tibetans" and "mountain machines."

Our trip to the Bhutanese Himalaya had been perfectly timed to witness both phases of the annual migration of the tribal people who live there. On our way up, we had passed several still-occupied summer tents at lower altitudes where the inhospitable temperatures were still further off. On the same day that we climbed the wet and misty mountain pass, we had been warmly welcomed into the tent of a herder family, occupied by three generations of Lingzhi people. We were given blocks of fresh yak cheese, pulled like pearls from strings along which they had been neatly placed and hung to dry. (Incidentally, the Lingzhi people are derived from ancestors who did not evolve the ability to digest milk throughout life and are therefore reliant on fermenting it—for example into cheese.)

Later that day, when I stood on the high pass looking through the gilded silver light across the browning vegetation to the soon-to-freeze turquoise lake, I was witnessing the recently abandoned summer grazing grounds of another tribal family. We were on our way to overnight with them in their winter house. I felt like I had traveled not only 17,000 feet up the Himalaya, but also thousands of years back in time.

What we next saw, within an hour of leaving the high mountain pass, reminded me of how wild that world is. Sprawled across the ground, like a forensic exhibit at a homicide scene, was the skeleton of a yak, fresh sinews still attached. We had diverted from the path to collect a camera trap—a waterproof device used in wildlife research that is triggered by movement to take a photograph—which Sonam had placed in the mountains several months before. When we examined the photos, we immediately identified the killer. It was a snow leopard, photographed at night, glowing iridescent blue in the electronic light of the night-sensitive camera. More than ever, I now understood why these mysterious and elusive animals are sometimes called "ghosts of the mountain."

Many hours later we arrived at our destination for the day. Having pushed our way through a herd of yaks, we approached a solid stone-built house set alongside a running stream. The mountain rocks of which it was built extended beyond the walls to the roof, lining strips of shiny silver sheets of corrugated steel, which were barely visible beneath. On either side of the front door, strips of yak meat hung drying on purpose-built racks suspended from the wall. Inside, the floor was made of broad, rough-hewn planks with a matching ceiling. Suspended from the thick wooden beams that supported the robust ceiling planks were rows and rows of stringed yak cheese, and in the middle of the room a small stove burning yak dung. Nearby was another stone building, the dairy, and in the distance beyond that, a small stone-built room containing a pit toilet.

As we sat around the fire that night, exhausted but warm and content, drinking tea and then eating a dinner of yak meat, barley, and chili-laden vegetables, our conversations ranged over many subjects. I learned that the daughter, a beautiful young woman who spoke good English, had a qualification in commerce. She and her husband had recently abandoned city life to return to the traditional lifestyle. When I asked why, she explained that she prefers the simple, quiet life and loves to be with her family in the mountains.

I also learned that the house had recently been refurbished, following an incident the previous summer. While the family was living in tents at the summer grazing grounds higher up the mountain, a bear had stripped off the roof, battered its way through the ceiling, and trashed the interior of the house. The new iron sheets, the rocks lining them, and the thick floorboard-like ceiling planks were measures to prevent this from happening again.

Most importantly, I learned that the resemblance of yak cheese to strings of pearls is not just visual. Yak cheese is precious to the mountain people—it is the product on which their livelihood depends. The strips lining the rafters were there partly to sustain them through the encroaching winter; but mostly, they would be loaded onto horses and transported for several days through the mountains to the nearest point of vehicle access. From there they would be driven to towns and cities and sold in the markets for cash.

Two days later we arrived at the rendezvous where cheese-laden horses meet the modern world. The contrast between what we saw there and the world through which we had trekked for the previous eight days was stark. Alongside a small, battered, corrugated iron-clad storage room, with a 20-inch carved wooden phallus projecting regally from the frame above the door, was a herd of horses resting, still blanketed and saddled, ready to return to the mountains. Nearby were sacks of yak cheese, carefully placed alongside a muddy, newly cut, unsurfaced road and a large yellow grader used for hauling logs. The slopes on either side of the road showed fresh scars of construction work. The phallus, I learned, was not a form of vulgar graffiti but an important cultural symbol believed to ward off evil.

When our four-wheel-drive arrived, it brought with it boxes of produce for the horses to take back into the mountains. The vehicle was unpacked and repacked with sacks of yak cheese to accompany us back to the town of Thimphu in the valley below.

I watched in silence as the newly arrived produce was distributed and laden onto the horses. There were sacks of grain, vegetables, bottles of oil, and bags of sugar, salt, and tea—all of which I had benefited from in accepting the hospitality of the mountain people. There were also many colorful packets of sugary and fatty foods—such as biscuits, instant noodles, and potato chips—decorated with garish pictures of smiling people enjoying them, and cartons of familiar pop-top soft-drink cans.

As we wound our way down the slippery, muddy road, through the habitat of the highest-living population of tigers on Earth, I couldn't help thinking about what I had just seen. The sugary and fatty processed foods and drinks that were on their way into the mountains were troubling. Into the strenuous lifestyle I had experienced over the previous eight days, these treats add diversity and pleasure and offer quickly accessible energy when it's most needed, which is often, given the active lifestyles of the mountain people and the cold temperatures in which they live. The snacks are also cheap, well-preserved, and—compared with water- and fiber-laden fruit and vegetables—lightweight and conveniently transported. But, I well knew, these same foods are wreaking havoc on food systems, cultural practices, and human health across the globe.

I'm not a superstitious man, but for a moment I caught myself hoping that that 20-inch phallus would do its job and protect the mountain people from what otherwise could rapidly destroy their healthy, 5,000-year-old pastoral lifestyle.

Two months later, I was on a small island in the Pacific Ocean witnessing my worst fear coming true. Together with my friends and colleagues, Olivier Galy, of the University of New Caledonia, and Corinne Caillaud, at the University of Sydney, I had traveled to Lifou, one of the Loyalty Islands situated off the east coast of the New Caledonia mainland. We had come to stay with a tribal family, the Zongos, and to experience directly the traditional family lifestyle and food system. But we were there mainly to examine a threat that was beginning to unravel that lifestyle, destroy the food system, and threaten the pristine island environment.

We stepped out of our rental car into the tropical paradise that is the Zongos' home. Greeted by their ebullient dog, contorting with excitement, I looked across the lush green lawn past the tropical fruit trees to a simple and welcoming house clad in fresh turquoise corrugated-iron sheets. On the veranda stood a well-built and handsome couple in their sixties, radiating health and happiness. They were Pierre and Naomi Zongo, our hosts.

We were first shown to our lodgings, a traditional round, thatched house. Inside the low doorway was a single space set around a large and majestic wooden pillar supporting a whorl of rafters hewn from logs. These were connected by a meshwork of stick purlins, creating a firm, umbrella-like structure supporting the thatched roof. Beneath that was a low circular wall, constructed in much the same way as the roof, with the thatch draped like a neatly cut blanket from the apex to the ground.

The inside was blackened by soot, accumulated over years of burning fires in the hearth beside the central pillar, and the air carried an earthy patina of fire, earth, and wood, not unlike a Scottish single malt whisky. On the floor, in beautiful contrast with the organically darkened walls and roof, were colorful woven mats on which our mattresses were placed. These houses, which are built by tribespeople, are reserved for special occasions, such as tribal meetings. I felt privileged to be there.

The following morning, we ate a breakfast of freshly made yogurt, with honey, papaya, and grated coconut picked from a tree nearby, and then traveled to the family gardens. We dug yams and potatoes from the rich brown soil, picked a variety of fresh vegetables, herbs, and tropical fruit from the large garden, and snacked on wild fruit and ruby red baby tomatoes that grew like weeds among the vegetable patches. We learned how Naomi and Pierre use a barrier of sharp-edged ground coral, like the white marking lines on a sports field, to protect their crops from slugs, and how plastic soda bottles placed on the metal fence posts surrounding the garden create a rattling sound that deters wild pigs.

We returned to feast on a lunch of *bounga*, a delicious Kanak dish made from local ingredients including yams, sweet potatoes, plantains, coconut milk, and fresh fish, all wrapped in a large envelope of banana leaves and baked for several hours in a traditional oven consisting of red-hot rocks and a hole in the ground. I had already seen the source of the vegetables and was next to experience firsthand how the fish are sourced.

After lunch, we helped Paul Zongo, Pierre and Naomi's son, who has a PhD and is the lead researcher on the project that brought us to New Caledonia, to prepare his fishing boat, then we headed into the ocean. The previous day, I had snorkeled off one of the beaches and so had some idea of what we were about to experience. Even there, close to shore, the ocean was teeming with life. Visibility was poor, but despite that, within minutes of swimming out, I saw a sea turtle, then a school of large pelagic fish, a bizarre spikey red lionfish, and scores of small colorful fish like confetti washing around the coral reefs.

Within a few hundred yards from where we had launched the boat, the sea drops to a depth of 300 feet, and not long thereafter to 1,000 feet deeper than that. Then we arrived at our first destination, a large coral structure, called Shelter Reef, that protrudes like a mountain from the depths. This combination of depth and structure, I well knew, is like a magnet for fish. And we weren't disappointed.

Not long after we arrived, we started seeing the characteristic swirling and splashing of large fish around the lures we were trolling out the back. Paul shouted and pointed as a powerful dolphin fish leapt clear of the surface in a failed attempt to eat our lure. The next to try was not so lucky. Paul stopped the boat as I hauled onboard 35 pounds of fresh fish, glistening gold and blue in the afternoon sun. Shortly, we had also caught a large trevally.

We next headed closer inshore to spearfish on shallower coral reefs. When I leapt into the water, I immediately knew that this was going to be special. Unlike the day before, where the water was murky from beach sand, providing only sneak glimpses of the creatures around me, now it was crystal clear and electric with life. On my first dive, as I headed down to orient myself to the world I had just entered, a large reef shark cruised past with the confident bearing of a nuclear submarine. Except, I noticed, it had a slightly edgy feel, one that I knew was associated with hunting. I was soon to see several more and knew that something was going on.

For a while I swam with the sharks, photographing them, and then headed out to find Paul and Olivier, who had headed toward the open ocean. I found them lying in wait alongside a large and deep channel teeming with fish, many swimming to stay in the same place against the strong current. At one point, two dogtooth tuna cruised past like a pair of toothy torpedoes. But we weren't the only ones hunting the channel. So, too, were the sharks. My research had previously taken me to Lizard Island, on the Great Barrier Reef in Australia, and I knew from experience that spearfishing near hunting reef sharks is to be done, if at all, with caution. They will seldom attack a human but will not hesitate to take a flailing fish off the end of a spear—and anything that comes in their way. Paul, who is experienced in those waters, speared a trevally, loaded it onto the boat, and the spearfishing was done for the day.

As we upped anchor and prepared to leave, we noticed what had caused the commotion. Around the corner from where we were hunting was a small tin boat with three young men on board. They were tribal people, friends of Paul, hunting fish to feed the mourners at a traditional funeral the following week. On board was a bin filled with reef fish—it was their hunting that had stirred up the sharks. One of the men held up a large fish, the size of a man's chest. It had been surgically cut through the middle in a gentle arc, the front and back halves joined only at the backbone. It was unmistakably a shark bite.

We gave the men our giant trevally and the trevally that Paul had speared as a contribution for the funeral and headed back to shore via Shelter Reef. En route, as the sun turned orange and the water inky blue, Olivier caught a dolphin fish of similar size to the one I had landed earlier, and Corrine caught a large barracuda-like predator called a wahoo.

When the sun dropped below the horizon, and we had wound in our lines, I sat thinking about conversations we had had earlier. There is very little commercial fishing off Lifou—what we were experiencing is subsistence fishing, to sustain families and provide communities with fish for ceremonial events like weddings and funerals. In the rich oceans off Lifou, this is sustainable and could continue indefinitely into the future, provided fishing practices don't change. If they do, and the commercial fishing fleets arrive to turn the ocean riches into cash, this will ring the death knell for a healthy and idyllic traditional lifestyle—one that is already under threat.

The following day we were to witness the problem firsthand. We traveled to We, the main town on Lifou, to see another side of island life. First, we stopped at the supermarket to pick up some supplies. The shelves were stocked with colorfully packaged processed foods—instant noodles, biscuits, and canned processed meats, to name just a few—which reminded me of the horses carrying junk food into the Bhutanese mountains as I drove through tiger territory. Most strikingly, there were hardly any fresh foods. Where, I wondered, were the vegetables and fish that had sustained us over the previous days in the Zongo household?

Perhaps, I thought, there was a separate market where fresh foods were sold. But there was none. We next visited a vegetable cooperative, set up several years ago to sell surplus produce from family gardens to the townsfolk. That, too, was surprisingly barren. There were shelves of yams, potatoes, and sweet potatoes, but except for a few pumpkins and a lone cabbage, nothing green, orange, yellow, or red. A problem, the friendly manager explained, is that families grow only enough produce for their own use and for ceremonial occasions. Instead, the townsfolk are turning to the packaged foods we saw on the supermarket shelves. Cheap and enjoyable, with devastating consequences.

With the new foods, fewer and fewer children are learning the skills of growing and harvesting fruit and vegetables in family gardens or catching fish. The market for imported processed foods is growing. And so, too, are waistlines and the numbers of people suffering from diabetes and other diet-related diseases.

In Bhutan, we saw the earlier stages of the same process—artificial foods making their way into the diets of traditional people. There is, as yet, no obesity among the yak herders partly because their access to these foods is still limited. With no stores or vending machines, they need to be transported in by horse. But in Lifou, which is accessible by boat and even has its own airport, no such restriction applies—overweight and obesity have increased by 13 percent since 2010, now afflicting more than 80 percent of adults. Likewise, obesity is on the rise in more accessible areas of Bhutan, the towns and cities from which processed foods are sourced to be taken into the mountains.

What we are seeing in both countries—repeating a pattern across the globe—are the earlier stages of a process that is ravaging countries like the United States and Australia. It is a "nutrition transition," in which traditional food environments based on farming and hunting are being replaced by those where foods are designed by chemists and food technologists to appeal to human appetites, then manufactured and shipped to every corner of the earth, always with the same consequences: skills associated with traditional feeding habits are lost, and obesity and associated diseases increase.

How and why do processed foods cause the problem? Can our work on insects, primates, and other species help to answer this question? That is the subject to which we turn in the next chapter.

CHAPTER 10 AT A GLANCE

1. When food environments change permanently, animals evolve new strategies to adapt to the changed circumstances. If the changes are too rapid or too extreme, the

adaptation involves crises of poor health, premature death, and even extinction.

2. Humans have used cultural means to change our food environments in several stages: the control of fire, the invention of tools, the transition from hunting and gathering to agriculture, and more recently the industrialization of food production and globalization of its distribution.
3. Globalization is causing unhealthy industrial foods to displace healthy traditional diets in cultures around the world, as they have in developed countries over several decades.
4. How have industrial foods affected human health?

11

Modern Environments

IT IS AN ODD TRUTH THAT OFTEN THE BEST WAY TO see something clearly is first to look away. This is exactly what we had done for one of the most important things in all our lives: our food environments.

For thirty years we had looked at locusts, cockroaches, cats, dogs, mink, and countless other animals in our labs; we had studied lubbers, crickets, monkeys, and apes in the wild; and we traveled up mountains and to remote islands to view places where several thousand years of human history collide with the modern world.

Now, as we turn back to our own species, we see more clearly than ever the central question: *Why, when we have the ability to create whatever food environment we want, have we created so much unhealthy nutrition, disease, death, inequality, and environmental degradation?*

We have also begun to see some answers.

An important step in our quest to understand how modern food environments became toxic was an e-mail David received from Brazil in 2015. It was from Professor Carlos Monteiro, an eminent public health nutritionist at the University of São Paulo. We already knew of the work that Carlos and his team were doing and had referenced it in our own papers. He was contacting us to say that he had read our study of the connection between human and pet eating patterns and saw its relevance to his own research.

Carlos has been studying the relationships between different types of foods and obesity across the globe. His studies, first in Brazil, then the United States and many other countries, have shown a clear pattern: the more people eat from a category called ultraprocessed foods, the more obesity exists. And, we already know, the more obesity there is, the more diabetes, heart disease, strokes, certain kinds of cancers, and premature death.

What are these ultraprocessed foods that are causing such havoc to our health? The short answer is that they are the selfsame, colorfully packaged foods that we saw in the previous chapter heading into the Bhutanese Himalaya and adorning the supermarket shelves of the idyllic Lifou Island in New Caledonia.

But for a problem so big, so complex, and so important, we need more than a short answer. We need to know how *ultra*processing differs from other forms of food processing, many of which pose no risk whatsoever and might even be good for us. This is where Carlos and his colleagues came in. They devised a system for defining different categories of foods according to their level of processing and for recognizing which processed foods endanger our health. The scheme is known as the NOVA system. There are four categories of foods in this system, distinguished by the nature of processing.

The first category, called NOVA group 1, consists of unprocessed foods and foods that are altered only in simple ways that leave their composition largely intact—for example, drying, crushing, roasting, boiling, pasteurization, removal of inedible parts, or vacuum packaging. The main aim of any processing in group 1 foods is to extend the life of foods, enabling them to be stored for longer, and to make their preparation for eating easier. Examples include pasteurized or powdered milk, canned or frozen vegetables, unsalted roasted nuts, and dried beans.

Unlike NOVA group 1, group 2 does not consist of whole foods but of culinary ingredients used in the preparation, cooking, or seasoning of foods. They include fats such as butter and oils, sugars and related products such as maple syrup, and salt. These ingredients are derived mostly through mechanical processes such as refining, extracting, pressing, or, in the case of salt, mining and evaporation.

The third NOVA group consists of processed foods but not deserving of the ultra label. These are made by adding group 2 ingredients, such as fat, sugar, or salt, to unprocessed or minimally processed group 1 foods, using preservation methods like bottling, canning, or in some cases fermentation. The main aims of this kind of processing are to increase the shelf life of the group 1 foods and increase their palatability. Examples include canned or jarred beans, vegetables, and fruits; canned fish; salted and sugared nuts; salted, dried or smoked meat; and freshly made traditional cheeses and breads.

The kinds of processing described in levels 1, 2, and 3 are not new. Some date back tens of millions of years to a period before the first human species evolved. In the previous chapter we saw an example of NOVA 1 processing by our distant cousin, the bearded capuchin monkey, which uses stone tools to remove the shells from otherwise inedible nuts.

NOVA groups 2 and 3—the extraction of culinary ingredients and their addition to unprocessed foods to extend their durability—are much younger than the first category and perhaps with a few arcane exceptions restricted to humans. But they, too, have been around for a very long time. Archaeologists have discovered evidence for olive oil extraction, cheese making, and bacon curing several thousands of years ago. In 2018, evidence of beer brewing dating to 13,000 years ago was discovered in a cave in Israel. In the same year, crumbs of charred bread were discovered at a hunter-gatherer site in Jordan, dating to over 14,000 years ago. Clearly, we have been processing food for a long, long time—even before the origins of agriculture. This makes the items in the first three NOVA categories unlikely suspects behind our modern nutritional disaster.

This is where NOVA group 4 comes in—the *ultra*processed foods.

These entered the scene only recently, since the growth of large-scale industry mechanized the production of everything from textiles to iron, steam engines, and ultimately motor vehicles. Perhaps no coincidence, at around the same time, the first weight-loss book was published in 1864—William Banting's *Letter on Corpulence, Addressed to the Public*. Recommending a low-carb diet, it was an instant best seller, going through six editions in two years and selling fifty thousand copies, an immense number for that time. Obesity, clearly, was on the minds of the public at the same time that ultraprocessed foods became a feature of the Victorian food environment.

What *are* NOVA group 4 foods? They are so extensively processed using industrial procedures that sometimes they are not even considered food, and referred to as "ultraprocessed *products."* They are industrial creations, no different from paint or shampoo, but designed to appeal to the consumer's palate rather than their decorative aesthetic or personal hygiene. Typically, their manufacture begins in large machines that separate whole foods into their components, such as starch, sugars, fats, oils, protein, and fiber. The raw materials involved are mostly industrially farmed high-yield crops, such as corn, soya, wheat, and sugar cane or sugar beet, and the ground or pureed carcasses of intensively farmed livestock. Some of these then undergo chemical modifications, including hydrolysis (a form of chemical breakdown) and hydrogenation (addition of hydrogen atoms), before they are combined with other substances. Along the way, the emerging products may undergo additional industrial processes such as pre-frying, extrusion, and molding, and be combined with chemical additives to extend their shelf life and alter their texture, flavor, odor, and appearance. Many of these chemicals are derived not from agriculture but from the petroleum or other industries.

If this sounds too bad to be true, it's not. Take one popular ultraprocessed food: ice cream. The August 17, 2016, edition of the magazine published by the global petroleum giant BP contained an article that began: *"What do ice cream, chocolate, paint, shampoo and crude oil have in common? Answer: the science behind them."*

The article explains how multidisciplinary teams of researchers at the BP Institute for Multiphase Flow in Cambridge (UK) are examining problems that are common across many industrial processes, from petroleum production to the manufacture of products such as paint, shampoo, chocolate (another ultraprocessed product), and ice cream. From a scientific perspective, bringing researchers together from different disciplines to examine big issues is a good thing. It is much the same approach that we take in our own institute, the Charles Perkins Centre, to understand the diverse forces driving the modern epidemic of obesity, diabetes, and heart disease.

Except that the common interests of the petroleum, shampoo, paint, and ultraprocessed food industries have nothing to do with improving human diets but rather with making products more efficient to produce or more appealing to consumers. And often, it is not only the challenges and interests that are shared by these industries but also the materials and processes that are used to solve the manufacturing challenges.

Take, for example, ice cream, which can be made at home using just cream, sugar, and fruit or other flavoring. Now consider the ingredients commonly used in the manufacture of mass-produced, commercial ice cream: *benzyl acetate,* a chemical that is also used in soaps, detergents, synthetic resins, and perfumes, and as a solvent in plastics and resins; *aldehyde C-17,* also used in dyes, plastics, and rubber; *butyraldehyde,* which is derived from the fuel gas butane and also used in the manufacture of pharmaceuticals, pesticides, and perfumes; *piperonal,* once used in hospitals to control head lice; *ethyl acetate,* also used in glues and nail polish remover. And the list goes on.

And commercial ice cream is not a trivial component of our diets. In 2018, 4.4 billion pounds of the stuff were eaten in the United States, about 13.5 pounds for every person. This is even more alarming when you remember that ice cream is just one category of ultraprocessed foods containing such ingredients, others being mass-produced candies, chocolates, cakes, breads, pizzas, chips, breakfast cereals, salad dressing, mayonnaise, ketchup, and too many more to mention.

In 2018, 61 percent of packaged foods for sale in Australia fell into NOVA group 4. The number of *new* food and beverage products offered for sale in 2016 alone was 21,435. Most of these were ultraprocessed products. Imagine, then, the cocktails of strange chemicals we are pumping into our bodies.

Whether or not these are doing us harm is an important question, but it is also a very complex one. Some of them probably are and others definitely so. In October 2018, for example, the US Food and Drug Administration banned the use of eight additives previously used as artificial flavorings in ultraprocessed foods, based on evidence from animal studies that they are carcinogenic. The substances are benzophenone, ethyl acrylate, eugenyl, methyl ether, myrcene, pulegone, pyridineoneone, and styrene (how's that for a recipe!). The first of these, benzophenone, is even banned from use in the manufacture of rubber intended to come into contact with food. At the time of writing this (June 2019) and possibly even at the time that you are reading it, these chemicals could still be at large in the food supply because their use remains legal for two years from the ruling. But you would have no way of telling which foods contain them: food manufacturers are not required to declare them on labels any more specifically than "artificial flavors."

All of these are artificial in the sense that they don't occur naturally in the foods to which they are added. Which is kind of obvious because even the foods themselves do not occur naturally—they are industrially manufactured ultraprocessed products. But some of these chemicals also occur naturally in foods from NOVA categories 1, 2, and 3. Myrcene, for example, is found in many plants, including wild thyme, cannabis, parsley, and hops. And yet, when used industrially in foods and perfumes, they are typically not from plants but synthesized chemically. Same molecule, different origin. Eugenyl is a component of many aromatic plants that are used in cooking, including cloves, bay leaves, basil, and nutmeg.

This tells us that, just because a chemical occurs naturally, does not mean that it's safe. In fact, many naturally occurring chemicals, including myrcene and eugenyl, evolved specifically *not* to be safe: they are produced by plants to dissuade herbivores from eating them.

Likewise, just because a chemical has a stern-sounding name and is artificially added to food, even if it is also used to kill lice, produce paint, or make plastics, that does not necessarily mean it is toxic. Take, for example, isoamyl acetate. This is used as an additive to mimic the flavor of banana in ice cream, candies, cakes, and various other ultraprocessed edibles; but it also moonlights as a paint and lacquer solvent and an additive in shoe polish. A bit off-putting, wouldn't you say? Except that the same chemical provides a pleasant fruity flavor to some styles of beer, even in Germany, where the famous Beer Purity Law (*Reinheitsgebot*) prohibits the use of anything other than water, grain, hops, and yeast. It is produced naturally by the yeast in beer, as a by-product of fermentation. It also, together with other chemicals, gives bananas their characteristic flavor. If we avoid this additive in ice cream, should we not also avoid beer and bananas? It is, after all, an identical molecule, whether added artificially to ice cream, excreted into beer by yeast, or synthesized naturally in bananas.

In other cases, processed food manufacturers overstep another boundary, adding artificially modified *molecules* to their concoctions. An infamous example of this is trans fats, which are produced industrially by the process of hydrogenation we mentioned above (adding hydrogen atoms) to healthy unsaturated oils from plants. One reason for doing this is that it makes cheaper liquid oils more solid so they can be used instead of butter to help crisp products like pizzas, pastries, microwave popcorn, and donuts. Altering healthy oils in this way also increases their shelf life and that of the ultraprocessed goods that contain them.

Unfortunately, it does nothing for the longevity of those who consume the crispy, long-lived delights. Health experts agree that industrial trans fats are the most toxic of all fats in our food supply, estimated by the World Health Organization to cause half a million deaths worldwide each year due to heart disease. And this is even though they are now banned in some high-income countries, led by Denmark in 2005, and followed by Iceland, Austria, and Switzerland. In 2018, the United States followed suit but only after some states, including New York, implemented their own bans. Subsequent studies in New York and Denmark showed significant reductions in hospital admissions and deaths due to heart disease. Trans fats are still a significant part of the food supply in many lower- and middle-income countries and even some richer ones. There is no ban in Australia, where we live, and no requirement for processed food manufacturers to state on labels whether and how much of this toxin they place in their products.

Confused by artificial additives? So are we. So many are used to produce ultraprocessed foods—more than three hundred are permitted for use in Australia—that there is no easy, or even possible, way to safely navigate these exotic cocktails. Some might be safe, others might be safe in some circumstances but not others, and others, like trans fats, are toxic whatever the circumstance. And even if we consumers *did* know enough about each of them to make sensible decisions about what to eat and avoid, that knowledge is of little use if the added chemicals are concealed behind secretive package labeling like "artificial flavors" (as in the recently banned additives in the United States) or there is no requirement to declare them on labels (trans fats in Australia). In that case, the best strategy might be to treat all ultraprocessed foods with suspicion.

Yet thirty years of studying animals in their natural food systems in the wild and creating artificial food systems to study them in the lab has shown us that the situation might not be as complex as it at first appears. Out of the chaos comes order when we view ourselves as just another species in just another food environment, albeit a rather peculiar one.

One thing that becomes obvious is that introducing ultraprocessed foods containing cocktails of new chemicals, or existing chemicals in new contexts, was destined to end in tears. Many of these substances are added not for their nutritional properties but as industrial shortcuts to reduce processing costs, increase shelf life, or improve the aesthetic appeal—flavor, crispness, color, and so on—of what otherwise would be unpalatable chemical gruel.

Exposing our meticulous human physiologies, which have evolved over millions of years, to such exotic new dietary ingredients was bound to be a lottery. Some, almost by happenstance, would turn out to be safe, some maybe even beneficial. But there was a good chance that others, perhaps many others, would pose a risk. This is why medicinal drugs are so thoroughly tested, via multiple stages, costing millions of dollars and taking many years, before they are approved for sale (or not). But there is no such rigor in the use of additives in the food industry.

As alarming as all that may be, there's another, more subtle, and even more frightening aspect than this lottery of toxicity, one that we should fear most. It is those properties of these products that their manufacturers ensure have very little to do with chance. They are deliberately designed into the foods to ensure one particular outcome: that we eat them in large quantities. And a good deal of the problem lies not with artificial additives but with subtle tweaks of the selfsame nutrients that our bodies need to stay alive.

To explain, we need to go back to our early experiments on locusts in little plastic boxes in the Oxford lab.

The point of our lab studies of insects was to understand how different mixtures of nutrients affected the animals. At the time, many scientists, particularly ecologists, had written about this topic and even done experiments to test their ideas. But there remained a lot of controversy and confusion, primarily for one reason. They had used real foods—such as leaves—either measuring their consumption by animals in the wild or bringing them into the lab for experiments.

A problem with this is that most foods consist of countless chemicals, and it is difficult to tell whether research results were due to the particular nutrient being studied, some other nutrient, or some specific combination of nutrients. This, we saw, was a real obstacle to finding what we were after.

For this reason, when planning the first locust experiments, we decided to avoid the complexity of real plants and make our own experimental foods, allowing us to precisely control their composition. We did this using ingredients ordered not from food suppliers but from chemical catalogs. These were products that had been industrially extracted from various sources, purified, and packaged for sale, principally for research, in containers labeled with chemical formulas, percent purity, and, in some cases, the raw materials from which they were produced. Among them were "bacteriological peptide," "casein," "egg albumin" (all proteins), "sucrose" and "dextrin" (both carbohydrates), "linoleic acid" (a fat), "Wesson's salt mix" (a vitamin blend), "cellulose" (indigestible fiber), and ascorbic acid (a preservative, which doubles as vitamin C). Armed with those ingredients, we could design specific food formulations and test their effects on the insects. In other words, we had created our very own ultraprocessed foods for scientific research.

Our experiments showed us something interesting. The more we came to learn how the insects responded to different diets, the more we could hack the locusts' biology to produce outcomes that nature never intended. We could cause animals to eat more or less, crave some foods but not others, grow quickly or slowly, be fat or thin, reproduce a lot or little, live for long or short, walk far or be lazy, and drink more or less water. As we later also showed in our big mouse experiment (Chapter 8), we could "dial up" just about any outcome we wanted just by tweaking the foods.

And we did all this not by adding exotic chemicals to the feed but by simply tweaking the mix of pure nutrients. Invariably, the most powerful ingredient was protein. If we increased this compared to carbs, we would cause one outcome in the lives of our subjects. If we decreased protein, we got another. By changing the mix of ingredients, with protein at the center, we could get locusts to eat five times more or less than they would otherwise! Through diet, we had immense power over the animals.

This got us thinking about human diets. Would we be just as susceptible to small tweaks in *our* nutrient mix? And if so, is protein the key factor, as it is with locusts and other species? This is why we were so excited when student Rachel Batley approached us, wanting to do experiments on her friends at her family's ski chalet. As we saw, we humans can also be easily manipulated by changes in protein proportions. It can leverage the intake of fats and carbs to the extent that if our diet contains too little protein, we will overeat and become fat.

But some important questions remained unanswered. Just because protein determined how much food we'd eat in experiments didn't mean it would do so in the real world, where we choose our foods from supermarket shelves, recipe books, and restaurant menus. It was for exactly this reason that we took our studies of animal feeding into the wild—into natural food environments—to see what happens in the realm of free choice.

And even *if* we proved that the dilution of protein causes humans to overeat in modern food environments, another question arose: *Which foods are diluting the protein content of our diet?* We had already answered this question for some other species—for example, we knew that for orangutans, fruits are the cause. When fruits are available, it takes a lot of energy consumption before the orangutans meet their protein target, and as a result they lay down considerable blubber.

But how about for humans? That e-mail from Carlos would lead us to the answers.

Some months after he first contacted us, Carlos and his PhD student, Euri Martinez Steele, suggested we collaborate in an analysis they were doing on the American diet. They were examining a huge dataset, information on the diets of 9,042 participants in the government-funded National Health and Nutrition Examination Survey (NHANES) of the United States. The goal of the analysis was to examine how eating different amounts of ultraprocessed foods affected the diets of Americans.

To do this, Euri and Carlos separated the participants into five groups based on the proportion of ultraprocessed foods in their diet: for group 1, 33 percent of their daily diet was contributed by ultraprocessed foods. Yes, one-third! And that was the *lowest* group. Group 2's diet was 49 percent ultraprocessed foods; group 3 was 58 percent; group 4 was 67 percent; and group 5 ate a staggering 81 percent ultraprocessed foods. And, because these were averages, it meant that many people in the fifth group ate *over* 81 percent ultraprocessed foods. The overall US average was 57 percent—more than half the diet, ultraprocessed "foods."

When we first saw these statistics, we were shocked, but we also saw an opportunity. We could build a model to test whether ultraprocessed foods play the same role for American humans as fruits do for orangutans in their forested food environment in Borneo—requiring high energy intakes in order to reach their respective protein targets.

As always, our first step in examining the results was to make a geometric plot with protein on the horizontal axis and carbs and fats on the vertical axis. The data made an almost perfect vertical line, meaning that as the proportion of ultraprocessed foods in the diet increased from groups 1 to 5, the percentage of calories from protein decreased from 18.2 percent to 13.2 percent. This was precisely what we had seen in the orangutan diet—the proportion of protein was high when fruits were scarce and low when they were abundant, while the amount of protein eaten remained the same. Also like orangutans, human energy intake increased in tandem with ultraprocessed food consumption, from 1,946 kcal (low ultraprocessed foods) to 2,129 kcal (high ultraprocessed foods). And yet, exactly like orangutans, there was no difference across all these groups in protein intake. They all kept eating until they hit their protein target.

The implications are sobering. It could suggest that the manufacturers of foods, whether consciously or not, veer toward low-protein recipes, and we respond by eating more—just as our locusts did when *we* reduced protein in their experimental foods. It's a perfect scheme for selling unhealthy food products, but, as Carlos's analyses had already shown, not so good if we are concerned about avoiding obesity, disease, and early death.

Our analyses, inspired all those years ago by experiments with locusts and then extended to primates in the wild, had provided a radical new insight into the obesity epidemic. Ultraprocessed foods make us fat *not* because we have such strong appetites for the fats and carbs they contain, as is often thought to be the case. Rather, we become overweight because our appetite for protein is *stronger* than our ability to limit fat and carb intake. So, when protein is diluted by fats and carbs, as it is in ultraprocessed foods, our appetite for it overwhelms the mechanisms that normally would tell us to stop eating fats and carbs. As a result, we eat more than we should, more than is good for us.

This revelation answered a lot of questions, but not all of them. Why, we wondered, does it take so many bizarre industrial formulations to make *us* fat, when orangutans and other primates need only fruit? Like protein leverage, the answer has its roots in our animal experiments.

In our telling of studies with locusts and other creatures, we've focused mainly on the importance of protein versus the other nutrients. What we haven't mentioned as much is another ingredient—which isn't a nutrient at all—that also played a major role in influencing how the animals ate.

Fiber.

Next to protein, fiber had the strongest effect on insect eating patterns. When fiber levels in their foods were low, any increase in it caused the locust to eat more overall. The reason is that adding fiber diluted the percentage of protein and carbohydrate; so, to maintain their intake of those two nutrients, the locusts ate even more, which meant they ate even *more* fiber. And it didn't take a PhD in biology to tell what they did with the extra fiber they ate. Within a few hours of feeding, we found, scattered around the experimental boxes, little pellet-like poos. The more fiber in their diet, the more of these deposits they left. The locusts were passing the fiber straight through the gut.

But beyond a certain point, this changed—with enough fiber in the diet, there was no further increase in eating. The fiber had filled the locusts; they had reached a point where their guts could process no more.

But what about the orangutans and us humans? The apes ate fruit until they became overweight, despite all the fiber they were getting. Humans, on the other hand, don't overeat fruit until we're obese—we get there by other means.

Let's explain this with a simple experiment. Try eating four apples, one after another. Most people wouldn't get beyond two before giving up. Now, compare this to drinking the juice of four apples—approximately a glass full. That's easy to finish, and it wouldn't be surprising if you could handle another four apples' worth. The difference is that by juicing it, the fruit has been stripped of most of its fiber, filtered out in the pulp. This is why the calories in sodas and other sugary beverages are so easily overconsumed—they slip down without activating the appetite brake.

We and the orangutans are cousin primates, but when it comes to eating fruit, we differ in an important way. Like many other herbivores, they have a gut that is specifically adapted to handling large volumes of dietary fiber. In orangutans, this consists of a huge, sack-like colon. Not only does the extra gut volume enable these apes to eat more fibrous fruit before filling up than humans can—together with all the sugars and fats it contains—but that anatomical difference also increases dietary energy in another way. Those orangutan colons house a huge microbiome comprising billions of bacteria whose function it is to digest fiber into usable calories.

Fiber explains why, unlike orangutans, we don't get as fat from eating fruit—we just can't consume as much as the apes can. It also helps to explain why we *do* get fat eating ultraprocessed foods. One of the main things that processing machines remove when converting tons of industrially produced crops into starch and sugar is fiber, which never makes its way back into the concoctions—not much of it, anyway. As we learned from locusts, mice, orangutans, and fruit juicers, removing fiber from foods is like cutting the brakes on our appetites. Now it's easy to understand why obesity and ultraprocessed foods have been inseparable partners through our recent history.

Before you blame the locusts for spoiling our party, there is one piece of good news they showed us. When we manipulated their diet and made them eat more carbs and fats, they also got more healthy micronutrients—vitamins and minerals—which came along for the ride. Could this be a silver lining to the cloud over our ultraprocessed diet?

Potentially, yes. In reality, no. Another casualty of the mass extraction machines, along with fiber, is micronutrients. Ultraprocessed foods contain very few vitamins and minerals to begin with, and eating a bit more of very little doesn't add up to much.

A cynic might conclude that lowering the protein in ultraprocessed foods and then removing fiber to increase the amount we *can* eat is a clever strategy to increase sales of these products. Possibly, but there are also other reasons for lowering the protein.

What might they be? We examined one in collaborative work with Professor Rob Brooks of the University of New South Wales.

This research involved no locusts, only a computer and internet connection. We went shopping at online supermarkets, in both the United States and Australia, and filled our virtual shopping carts with 106 food products found in both countries. We then priced them and noted the nutrient content of each food. These numbers enabled us to calculate how much the price of each product is influenced separately by its fat, carbohydrate, and protein content.

In both countries, the results were the same. The fat content had little effect on the price of foods, with each calorie from this nutrient increasing the price by a very small amount. Protein, on the other hand, had a strong influence: the more protein, the more expensive were the products. Surprisingly, carbs actually *reduced* the cost: as the carbs increased, the foods became cheaper! It's easy, then, to see why a processed food manufacturer might be stingy with protein and liberal with the fats and carbs—doing so could reduce manufacturing costs. The bonus, as we have shown, is that doing so also hacks our appetites, causing us to overeat.

These two explanations, reducing production costs and increasing consumption via protein leverage, might seem sufficient to explain why ultraprocessed foods have low protein and high fats and carbs. Except there's an even more compelling benefit: taste.

Once again, our noble locusts illustrate it. When given the choice between a high- and low-fiber food, they ate the version with less fiber. That's because fiber dilutes the presence of nutrients, and nutrients—fats, carbs, and protein but also salt—are important for the flavor of foods. Low fiber means better taste. Our early work on locust taste proved this: when we increased the concentration of nutrients that hit the taste buds, the rate at which electrical signals hit the insects' brains also increased, thereby causing the locusts to eat.

It's easy to see then why reducing the fiber content of ultraprocessed foods benefits the manufacturers—it makes their products taste better than they would otherwise.

So the same effect we observed in locusts helps explain one of the biggest health crises in history: the rise of ultraprocessed foods. It illustrates how the two drivers of our diet—what foods we choose to eat and how much of each we consume—have worked together to drive the crisis.

Low fiber and high fats and carbs make foods tasty, causing us to choose them over healthier alternatives. At the same time, the low protein content of these foods makes them cheapest to produce. And the combination of low protein, low fiber, and low cost causes us to overeat—the final triumph of ultraprocessed foods.

Ultraprocessed foods, therefore, play a role for our species similar to that of fruits for orangutans in the natural forests of Borneo: they are an abundant source of energy, low in protein, high in fats and carbs—a perfect diet for gaining weight.

There are important differences, though. One is that orangutans have a very good reason for storing fat: when the fruits are gone, the fat stores help the apes survive long periods of energy scarcity. For most humans in industrialized food environments, there is no equivalent. There is no period of food shortage and so no benefit from storing fat. We eat our ultraprocessed foods year-round.

Another difference is that orangutans have become adapted over millions of years to the fruits they eat. Ultraprocessed foods resemble nothing we've ever eaten in the history of our species. They are low in healthy micronutrients and fiber and adulterated with hundreds of chemicals that never were intended to be eaten in large quantities—if at all—by humans. Ultraprocessed foods are displacing our natural diets, with devastating consequences.

We would be happy to leave it there, but there's a final twist to the story. Industrial processing is not the only means through which protein, fiber, and micronutrients in our diets are being diluted by extra carbs. This has been happening over the past

10,000 years, since the beginning of agriculture—it has been one of the consequences of domesticating crops.

Recently, an even more alarming cause has been discovered. Rising carbon dioxide in the atmosphere, produced by all our industrial activity, is having exactly the same effect as domestication and ultraprocessing: increasing carbs and decreasing protein, fiber, and micronutrients in our staple food crops. The mechanism is simple. In plants, carbon dioxide is the raw material that traps the energy from sunlight to form sugar and starch. The more of it they get, the more sugar and starch are formed, and all of the sugar and starch dilutes the protein, micronutrients, and fiber.

Do food manufacturers admit that they design their products specifically to make us overeat? No, they say, they have simply given us foods that are tasty, convenient, and cheap, which if eaten in moderation can form part of a healthy diet. The fault is with us for having abused those foods and brought about our current predicament.

Or so they say. Except that there are plenty of facts to suggest otherwise.

CHAPTER 11 AT A GLANCE

1. The category of foods that bears the most responsibility for the epidemic of obesity and associated diseases is ultraprocessed foods—industrial products that are manufactured from highly processed and artificial ingredients.
2. Ultraprocessed foods are typically low in protein, fiber, and micronutrients and high in fats, unhealthy carbs, and added flavor enhancers—exactly the circumstances that our animal studies suggested will cause overeating and poor health.
3. So why do we take so readily to processed diets to which our bodies are poorly adapted?

12

A Unique Appetite

THE PROTEIN APPETITE PLAYS A POWERFUL ROLE in driving the global obesity epidemic. Yet there's an appetite, possessed only by our own species, that is even stronger than the protein appetite. And of all appetites, this bears the most responsibility for our nutrition crisis.

It's the appetite for profit.

In our modern environment, food is a commercial commodity upon which industries, companies, supply lines, investments, careers, and livelihoods have come to rely. But food is different from other commodities in important ways.

Number one is that we all need it. Unlike most purchases—we could choose to buy books or not, own a car or use public transport, rent rather than buy a house, and so forth—there is no alternative to eating. Which puts the food industry in an enviable position: they sell a product that everybody needs.

Still, food producers face a massive economic challenge: how to grow the market. For television sets, motor vehicles, luxury yachts, and computers, the task is straightforward—get more people to buy them, get existing customers to buy more than one, or get customers to replace them more often. Not so with food. All humans already eat it, and there's a limit to how much each of us can consume. Other strategies are needed to maintain the food industry, to keep it profitable, keep it growing, and satisfy the shareholders.

One strategy is to add value to the products they sell and in this way make them more profitable. Inexpensive raw materials are processed and mixed with other ingredients, the mixtures processed some more, wrapped in colorful packaging, and sold for much more than the price of the ingredients. We couldn't put it more succinctly than did Michael Pollan: "transform a few pennies' worth of grain and sugar into five dollars' worth of breakfast cereal."

Equally important is ensuring that these profitable foods outcompete the alternatives offered by other companies. This process, called *increasing market share*—sometimes known in food industry circles as *stomach share*—is a powerful force that shapes our food environment. It results in an arms race where each side takes ever bolder steps to outdo the others. In weaponry, the result is an ever more dangerous world. In processed food, the plan is to outdo the competition in price, convenience, and attractiveness. But the end result can be the same.

We already have seen some of the strategies used in the wrestle for market share. Cocktails of chemicals are added to improve the color, texture, flavor, odor, shelf life—and other properties—of these products, and the mixtures are packed with cheap fats, carbs, and salt. The high levels of fats and carbs not only make the mixtures tastier, especially when stripped of flavor-diluting fiber, but they also replace expensive protein, making them cheaper to produce.

One strategy is to bring a product to peak tastiness, called the *bliss point*. In a telling example, industry-employed mathematician and experimental psychologist Howard Moskowitz created no fewer than fifty-nine varieties of Dr Pepper soda and ran three thousand taste tests across the United States. The results enabled him to identify the exact formula that provided the tastiest product. Being soda, a key ingredient was sugar. In other foods it's more complex, involving mixtures of fat, sugars, and salt. Some products include artificial flavorants to make cheap, starchy, and fatty foods, such as potato chips, taste savory like protein. What all these products have in common is that they are engineered to outprice and out-taste the competition.

A sure method to increase stomach share is to buy out the competition. In this way, food companies have become fewer and larger. It might not appear so, judging from the countless brands of processed foods offered for sale. But the diversity is more apparent than real. Almost all of these products are produced by just nine massive multinational companies. One of these, Nestlé, owns over two thousand brands.

Large companies have strong advantages over smaller competitors. An obvious benefit is more customers, but they also have cheaper production costs due to economies of scale. Processed foods are therefore immensely profitable. In 2017 Nestlé recorded in its annual report total sales of over $87 billion. This is greater than the economic activity (gross domestic product, or GDP) in that year for 128 different countries! Only 63 nations produced goods and services that exceeded Nestlé's sales revenue. In the same year the company reported a profit of $14.3 billion, more than the GDP of 71 countries.

Revenue, clearly, is not in short supply in the Big Nine processed-food companies. With those levels of cash comes immense power to influence our food environment and change the way we eat, for better or for worse.

One way this power is exercised is to reach into the minds, wallets, and stomachs of us all through advertising. According to its 2017 annual report, PepsiCo spent $2.4 billion on advertising. And yet it was outdone by its main competitor, the Coca-Cola Company, which is reported on the website notesmatic.com to have spent $3.96 billion. Statista, a provider of market information, reports that the 2017 advertising bill of Nestlé was $7.2 billion. To put that into perspective, in 2009 the total annual spending on nutrition research, across all U.S. governmental agencies, was $1.5 billion. Each of these companies spends more on influencing what we eat than the government spends researching the consequences of these influences.

There are many clever and effective strategies used in the marketing of processed foods, too many to consider here. But we will briefly consider two: marketing to children and the aptly named "health halo."

For food companies, children are a gold mine. There are, to begin with, many of them, and they have a surprisingly high spending power. In 2015, there were fifty million kids in the United States age 11 and under, estimated to wield a mouthwatering $1.2 trillion. This is partly through direct spending but also in their ability to influence the purchasing decisions of their parents. And that's just the beginning. The greatest advantage is that children's eating choices tend to stick with them for life and may even be passed on to their children. Today's childhood choices shape tomorrow's national diet, and every food company wants to be a big part of that.

This explains why huge sums are spent by food companies in marketing to children. One route is through television. TV ads are highly effective partly for reasons noted in a 2004 report of the American Psychological Association: young children lack the ability to distinguish commercials from program content—eating this or that brand of sugar-, salt-, and fat-laden product becomes associated with the fantasy world they are drawn to for entertainment. What better result than embedding a product in the fantasy world of children?

As television watching has declined and computer activities, such as gaming, have increased, the blurring of commercial and entertainment content has become even more brazen. Now junk food marketers aggressively blend their products into games so food is not only associated with, but is itself a part of the fantasy world. The product itself is part of the entertainment experience—the fantasy is crafted around the food. This is most insidious of all because designers can direct the way the child interacts with the world of the product, in this way forming lasting positive associations, even literal friendships, with the brand. These so-called "advergames" are a marketer's dream; as one marketing expert noted, they enable companies to associate their brand with "something that people are doing for stress relief and fun, making for a positive brand association." Not surprisingly, their impact on sales—and diets—outstrips more traditional approaches.

Although it's difficult to get a direct measure of exactly how successful a particular advergame is, less than two weeks after burger chain Hungry Jack's released its version in Australia, a spokesperson for the advertising company was quoted saying, "It has been a huge success, with over one million downloads and accounting for several million dollars' worth of incremental revenue." That's a lot of burgers, fries, and shakes.

Children are particularly susceptible to these tactics because the part of our brains that controls whether we respond impulsively to temptation is not fully developed until early adulthood. Impulsive responses are, of course, not unknown among adults either but they are more likely to think—even if only fleetingly—about the long-term health consequences of dietary choices. Food marketers, well aware of this, have crafted their strategies accordingly.

One of the most cynical of all is the "health halo" effect. With the rise of obesity and nutrition-related diseases, many people have become increasingly conscious of their dietary choices. The food industry—the same companies that have caused the problem—now exploit this, using images, terms, and claims that associate processed foods with health. The end result is that well-meaning consumers, making an effort to feed themselves and their children the right things, are lured into eating more of the same: harmful processed foods.

How do the marketers do it? Something as seemingly innocent as the coloring of the food packaging can play a role. One study showed that when offered exactly the same candy bar, with either a red or a green calorie label, people judged the green-labeled version to be healthier. Perhaps no coincidence, then, that as part of its health-promoting Guideline Daily Amounts campaign, candy company Mars Incorporated used green calorie labels on the front of the packaging. The company explained that they chose green because it was a "clear favorite with consumers." Cornell communications researcher Jonathan Schuldt has speculated that this preference could reflect the fact that green labels might cause consumers to perceive candy in a healthier light than they normally would.

Often, food packages display words or images that conjure up associations of well-being. A study in Australia analyzed the labels of 945 sugar-containing beverages for health-associated imagery. Despite their high sugar content and low nutritional value, over 87 percent of them had words or images implying that they were healthy. Most had pictures or mention of fruits or words such as *natural, pure, raw, fresh, real* that we associate with proper foods. Others referred explicitly to nutrition ("no cholesterol," "unsweetened," "nutritional") or to health ("wellness," "healthy"). Many studies have shown that associations such as these can increase the consumption of foods. One, for example, showed that people ate more "fruit chews" than "candy chews," even though these were exactly the same product. In another, breakfast cereals labeled as containing "fruit sugar" were perceived to be healthier than those labeled as containing "sugar."

Such word games are rife in the marketing of processed foods. Some brands of rice proudly announce on the packaging "cholesterol-free"—but of course *all* rice is cholesterol-free. Just as there are candies labeled "99% fat-free," diverting us from the fact that they are sugar-laden and filled with artificial substances. And the terms *light* or *lite* could refer to virtually anything, including color, flavor, texture, or fat content. And *multigrain* bread is often no different than refined white bread, with a few seeds or grains added, and is certainly no healthier. And so the list goes on. For the consumer, the only thing that seems sure about the messaging on processed foods is that it is designed not to inform but to misinform and manipulate.

Surely, we can rely on government policy and legislation to help us to make healthy eating choices? In theory, yes. Most countries have laws against misleading advertising and appoint panels of expert scientists to assess the best available information and formulate national dietary guidelines. But in practice, even these are not free from the immense power of the food industry.

For this, it had a good mentor—the tobacco industry. In 1954, as evidence was beginning to emerge that cigarette smoking causes lung cancer, the tobacco companies banded together to publish, in 488 newspapers in 258 cities, an ad headlined "Frank Statement to American Smokers." The document was designed to comfort the smoking public, saying, "Although conducted by doctors of professional standing, these experiments are not regarded as conclusive," "medical research of recent years indicates many possible causes of lung cancer," "there is no proof that cigarette smoking is one of the causes," and "we believe the products we make are not injurious to health." It assured the public that health was "paramount to every other consideration in our business" and pledged a number of measures to safeguard it.

In fact, subsequent studies have shown that the "Frank Statement" was designed by a public relations firm to cast doubt on the scientific evidence and manipulate the public's perception of the risks of smoking. As noted by researchers Kelly Brownell and Kenneth Warner, "It was a charade, the first step in a concerted, half-century-long campaign to mislead Americans about the catastrophic effects of smoking." What followed were decades of deceit and ploys to undermine the research, manipulate policy, and instill false confidence in the public about the safety of their product. The strategy was carefully planned. In the words of former Food and Drug Administration commissioner David Kessler:

> Devised in the 1950's and '60s, the tobacco industry's strategy was embodied in a script written by lawyers. Every tobacco company executive in the public eye was told to learn the script backwards and forwards, no deviation was allowed. The basic premise was simple—smoking had not been proved to cause cancer. Not proven, not proven, not proven—this would be stated insistently and repeatedly. Inject a thin wedge of doubt, create controversy, never deviate from the prepared plan. It was a simple plan and it worked well.

The tobacco industry is not alone in challenging evidence and casting doubt. In 2012, the American Beverage Association asserted, "Sugar sweetened beverages are not driving obesity" (reported in the *Los Angeles Times*, 21 September 2012)." In the same year, a senior Coca-Cola executive, Katie Bayne, made the staggering claim, "There is no scientific evidence that connects sugary beverages to obesity" (*USA Today*, 8 June 2012). In their aptly named book, *The Merchants of Doubt,* historians Naomi Oreskes and Erik Conway show how sowing mistrust in science has become an industry in its own right. We see the same kind of campaigns against scientific evidence for global warming, pesticide harm, and other current manmade perils. In many cases, it involves not only calling into question the scientific conclusions but actively manipulating them.

This practice is not new. Industry documents reveal that in 1954, the Tobacco Industry Research Committee received a letter from Robert Hockett, head of research at the Sugar Research Foundation. He was writing to tell the cigarette makers that he had devised a clever strategy that might be of interest to them. He had organized research projects in medical schools, hospitals, and universities that "exonerated sugar of most of the charges that had been laid against it." Hockett was later hired as the tobacco industry group's assistant science director.

Scientific articles funded directly by the food and beverage companies are four to eight times more likely to produce conclusions that support the financial interests of the funding company than is independent research. We are working with a team, led by our colleague at Charles Perkins Centre, Professor Lisa Bero, studying the influence of industry on nutrition research. It is a complex process where the outcome can be biased at several stages of the research, including the question being asked, how the research is designed, how it is conducted, and whether part or all of the results are published.

How do companies benefit from casting doubt on the scientific evidence associating their products with bad health outcomes? An obvious benefit is that it discourages consumers from shifting their preferences elsewhere. Nobody wants to die of lung cancer, diabetes, or heart disease.

Equally important, it helps the companies in one of their major challenges, to avert and undermine effective public health policies and programs that could curtail their commercial interests. One way they do this is through political lobbying: industry groups employ representatives, often with prior experience in government, to gain access to decision-makers in an attempt to influence food-related policy in their favor. For them to succeed, casting doubt on unfavorable scientific conclusions, or concocting more favorable conclusions, is essential. In 2015, processed-food manufacturers are reported to have spent $32 million on lobbyists, which was money well spent. This kind of paid governmental advocacy has done magic for the industry.

One example is when it turned pizza into a vegetable. It all started in 1981 when, in an attempt to cut school lunch budgets while appearing to meet dietary guidelines, the Reagan administration insisted that condiments like pickle relish and ketchup should be counted toward the recommended vegetable servings. In 2011, under Obama, the Department of Agriculture attempted to overturn this.

Seeing the risk, the junk food industry immediately responded by investing $5.6 million in a lobbying campaign. The two companies that spent the most had large contracts for french fries and pizzas in school lunches. It worked. Congress passed a bill that stopped the Department of Agriculture from enforcing any policies that affected how the tomato paste in pizza and potatoes in fries count as nutritional contributions to daily requirements. The press enjoyed reporting that Congress had classified pizza as a vegetable.

Equally magical, some would say, is how a "balanced diet" came to mean a diet that balances human health with the commercial interests of the food industry.

Every five years, the US Department of Agriculture and US Department of Health and Human Services performs a review of the scientific evidence on the links between diet and health. Based on this evidence, these agencies issue dietary guidelines to advise Americans how to eat a balanced, healthy diet. This, of course, involves eating more of some foods and less of others. Simple as that sounds, it has proved anything but.

The science, needless to say, presents some challenges, but by and large these agencies do a pretty good job of identifying the foods that Americans should be eating more of and those they should be eating less of. Unsurprisingly, the "eat mores" include minimally processed, plant-derived whole foods, such as fruit, vegetables, beans, nuts, whole grains, and sources of healthy fats including vegetable oils and fish. The guidelines are very clear on this. In the latest guidelines (2015–2020), for example, all six of the bullet-pointed "Key Recommendations" on things that should be increased in the diet are devoted to these food groups.

The problem is that obesity and associated diseases cannot be prevented simply by eating *more* of anything; for that we also need to know which foods to eat *less* of. Yet the guidelines are conspicuously vague on what these are. There is, for example, not a single food listed in the "eat less" section of the Key Recommendations for the 2015–2020 guidelines. All the advice for that involves specific nutrients: added sugar, saturated fats, sodium (salt), and alcohol. This is not bad advice: if Americans cut down on the intake of these, there would be significant health benefits. But it is not particularly useful advice because it does not say which *foods* should be reduced in the diet to make way for healthy alternatives. And it is not as if the science itself is unclear on this. Among the foods that need to be reduced in the American diet are highly processed industrial foods and red meat, especially processed meats.

This eat more–biased dietary advice is not restricted to the 2015–2020 version; it has been a consistent feature of the Dietary Guidelines for Americans since they were first issued in 1980. We believe the reason is not based on science; it is political. The US Department of Agriculture, as its name implies, is not primarily a health agency; its main responsibility is to oversee the American farming industry. This includes stimulating rural development, overseeing "commodity checkoff programs" designed to promote the sales of particular agricultural commodities, and administering subsidies that help ensure the profitability of large agricultural monocultures. Among these is corn, the stuff that supplies feed for the large industrial meat farms and the raw materials for the ultraprocessed food industry. As one journalist observed, having the same agency that is responsible for American agribusiness also telling Americans what they should eat is like having the fox guard the henhouse.

This should make it clearer why specific foods feature prominently in the guidelines on what to eat more of but are nowhere to be seen when it comes to what to eat less of: "eating more" is compatible with the commercial interests of the agrifood complex, but eating less is not. And should the USDA momentarily forget it, they will quickly be reminded, as happened in the debacle over the dietary pyramid.

In the 1980s, the relevant branch of the department decided that it would be helpful to produce a guide that translated nutrient-based research into a graphic that provided practical advice about which foods people should eat and how much of each. The team decided on a pyramid, which consumer research had shown to be the design that most clearly communicated that some food groups, those at the broad base, should contribute most to a balanced diet, while those at the tip should contribute least. Associated with each category of food was text stating the recommended number of servings per day.

In February 1991, following several years of work on the project, including extensive consultations with nutrition experts, presentations at professional conferences, and exhaustive internal review in the USDA, the pyramid and associated report had been sent to the printers for a March publication date. So certain were its creators of the imminent launch that the pyramid had been discussed extensively with the media, and thirty publishers had been notified to ensure its inclusion in textbooks.

But, as explained by Professor Marion Nestle in her book *Food Politics,* it never happened. The March publication date came and went, and in April the USDA announced that the pyramid had been withdrawn. Its justification was that it needed further testing on low-income adults and schoolchildren. Subsequent research has suggested otherwise—that it had been withdrawn because the meat and dairy industries had complained that their slice of the pyramid was too narrow and placed immediately beneath the no-go "fats, oils, and sweets." They preferred a bowl-shaped graphic, which suggested greater equivalence among the food groups.

A year later and following $855,000 worth of additional research, the pyramid was finally released. But it was changed from the original version in a way that had nothing to do with low-income adults and schoolchildren. The recommended number of servings per day of meat and dairy had been changed from 2–3 to *at least* 2–3 and was set in bold typeface.

As this account shows, the power of the food industry is such that it can help shape both the nature of our food environment and the advice we receive on how to keep healthy in it.

This brings us to one final strategy that some players in both the processed food and the tobacco industries have employed in their relentless bid for market share. It is to blame the victims—transfer the responsibility for the damage their products cause to consumers.

In 1996, after it had been discovered that even secondhand smoke could cause cancer, a woman publicly asked the chairman of tobacco and food company RJR Nabisco, Charles Harper, whether he would want people smoking around his children and grandchildren. Mr. Harper's response was "I would not intrude on the right of any of them to smoke, but I would try to discourage them" and "If the children don't like to be in a smoky room . . . they'll leave." Persisting, the woman pointed out that an infant cannot leave a room, to which Mr. Harper's response was "At some point they learn to crawl, okay? And then they begin to walk." Later, Harper said that by making an obviously ridiculous statement he had hoped to dramatize parents' important role in the issue.

In a similar vein, in 2002, when the then-president of the National Restaurant Association, Steven Anderson, was asked about the role of restaurants in the obesity epidemic, his response was, "Just because we have electricity doesn't mean that you have to electrocute yourself."

Mr. Anderson, of course, is right. But then we should remind ourselves that none of the eleven million people who die annually across the world of diet-related diseases *deliberately* eat themselves to death. Another point: the safe use of electricity is strictly regulated by rules and codes, which are set not by manufacturers of electrical equipment but by independent experts with the public in mind.

Perhaps now it will be clearer why we are so concerned about the ultraprocessed foods making their way into the mountains of Bhutan and the supermarket shelves of the tropical island paradise of Lifou. The manufacturers of processed foods have immense power for exercising their insatiable appetite for market share. They have done so with enviable effectiveness, now accounting for 57 percent of the average American diet, with half of the population eating even more than that and one-fifth as much as 81 percent. It's easy to see where all this is headed—more illness, more misery, more profits.

How, as individuals, can we respond? What we have tried to equip you with to this point is one of the most powerful tools of all: awareness. Once you are aware of *why* ultraprocessed foods are so appealing, what underlies all the attractive messaging about them, and what they are doing to our health, you will be in a much better position to make your own decisions about diet. In the final chapter, we'll take it a step further and offer practical advice for how to safely make your way through the current—perilous—food environment.

First, we need to go back to biology to discover the final clue to our mystery: a vicious cycle.

CHAPTER 12 AT A GLANCE

1. Big multinational food companies have devised clever strategies to ensure that their highly profitable ultraprocessed food products are sold and eaten in large quantities—no matter the public health consequences.
2. These include aggressive marketing, including to children, and misleading labeling suggesting health benefits or concealing health risks.
3. They have also adopted some of the strategies developed by the tobacco industry, including distorting scientific evidence on the dangers of their products and influencing government policy and public health advice such as dietary guidelines.
4. How can we resist these powerful influences?

13

Moving the Protein Target and a Vicious Cycle to Obesity

WE HAVE SEEN IN THE PREVIOUS CHAPTERS HOW the deluge of ultraprocessed foods and beverages has led to a decrease in the overall concentration of protein in the modern food environment. Fiber has been removed and protein has been replaced by calorie-rich, inexpensive fats and carbs. As a result, we have become trapped by our powerful protein appetite into eating more calories than we need. Our protein appetite, which evolved to help us navigate toward optimal nutrition in our ancestral food environments, has become something of a liability. This is bad enough on its own. But there is a final twist to the sorry saga, which makes it even worse.

Something about the development of obesity across the world didn't quite add up. If the obesity epidemic were simply the result of our being tricked into eating more calories by ultraprocessed foods and beverages, weight gain should have risen but then leveled off. This is because bigger bodies require more fuel—about 24 kcal more per extra kilogram—and so the more we weigh, the more calories we burn.

However, weight gain and obesity have *not* slowed or hit a plateau. Over the past five decades, we have eaten progressively more than we need at every size, fueling ever greater weight gain. Something is compelling us to eat more calories than we require at every weight, even as waistlines have expanded and BMI has risen. The evidence is that this something is protein. Bigger bodies don't just need more calories; they require more protein. To explain why, we'll need to dip into the science of something called *protein turnover*.

As we've seen throughout this book, each living thing has an intake target for the amount of protein it needs. This requirement is set by two factors. The first is the demand for amino acids for muscle growth, tissue maintenance, and other bodily functions. The second is the rate at which you break down and lose protein from your body. It's like trying to fill a bathtub with a leaky drain: the more protein that is lost down the drain, the more must be eaten to fill the tub to the target level.

There are two main routes of loss for protein. One is when your body starts to break down muscle tissue, releasing amino acids into the blood system. The other is when the liver starts to use some of those amino acids from muscle breakdown, as well as others absorbed into the bloodstream from digested food in the gut, not for building new body proteins but to produce glucose for energy.

Together, this sounds like a drastic combination, and indeed it is. It's usually seen only under starvation conditions. This is because, unlike fat tissue, which is the body's main fuel storage, we don't store protein except in our muscles and other lean tissue. Consuming these as fuel is a last resort. It's like burning the furniture to keep your house warm—something you'd do only if the firewood is gone and you are freezing to death.

As you might expect, the body has a mechanism to spare the furniture unless its burning is absolutely necessary. The hormone insulin is the signal that indicates there's no need to burn the furniture. Insulin blocks protein breakdown in muscle and stops the liver from using amino acids to make glucose. It's a clever mechanism because insulin is secreted from the pancreas into the blood in response to a rise in blood sugar after a meal. When insulin is released, your body knows you have eaten and have glucose to burn. There is no need to break down protein and amino acids.

However, even clever mechanisms can go badly wrong. When there's a chronic excess of calories being eaten and body weight is rising, the responsiveness of our tissues to insulin gradually falls—they become insulin resistant. They start to ignore its signal. As a result, the pancreas must release more insulin to get the same effect. This is the beginning of the process leading to type 2 diabetes. But even before then, we're in trouble.

As the muscles become less responsive to insulin, they release more amino acids from protein breakdown, and at the same time the liver becomes more prone to turn amino acids into glucose. This means that more protein must be eaten to rebuild the muscles that are being broken down. To return to our bathtub analogy, the drain has become leakier.

We can see the result of this today. As the protein target of populations has crept up almost imperceptibly with growing body size and increased prevalence of insulin resistance, the appetite for it has driven a progressive increase in calorie intake, keeping BMI ever on the rise. Look at the table below, where we have listed a series of hypothetical values for the protein target—from 55 to

Protein target (g per day)	**Calories needed to be eaten on a percent protein diet of:**					
	10%	**12%**	**15%**	**17%**	**20%**	**25%**
55	2200	1833	1467	1294	1100	880
60	2400	2000	1600	1412	1200	960
65	2600	2167	1733	1529	1300	1040
70	2800	2333	1867	1647	1400	1120
75	3000	2500	2000	1765	1500	1200
80	3200	2667	2133	1882	1600	1280
85	3400	2833	2267	2000	1700	1360
90	3600	3000	2400	2118	1800	1440
95	3800	3167	2533	2235	1900	1520
100	4000	3333	2667	2353	2000	1600

100 grams per day, which is a difference of 45 grams, or 180 kcal. To achieve that modest increase in protein intake would require eating 1200 extra kcal on a 15 percent protein diet! A small change in protein intake drives a large change in energy consumed. The size of this effect is even greater on a lower-protein diet. Compare, for example, the energy needed to get from 55 to 100 grams of protein on a 12 percent protein diet: 1,833 versus 3,333 kcal—a difference of 1,500 kcal.

You can see now why the combination of a rising protein target and a declining percent protein in the modern diet has been catastrophic for the world's waistline.

Our need for protein doesn't vary solely due to insulin resistance. It changes from birth to old age and varies with lifestyle and several other factors. Could we measure changes in protein targets of humans and assess their importance for health? Thanks to collaborations with our pediatrician and dietitian colleagues, we have now done just that.

It was September 2010 and Steve had just given a talk to a pediatric endocrinology conference in Perth, Australia. Immediately afterwards, two members of the audience were keen to discuss possible research collaborations. Professor Roger Smith from the University of Newcastle, north of Sydney, was intrigued by our work on slime molds and wondered whether there were lessons for his research into the development of the placenta during pregnancy. He also wanted to know whether Nutritional Geometry might help with results from a study of pregnant women and their newborn babies. That was an exciting prospect—and an easier problem to begin with than comparing slime molds to the human placenta.

Another audience member, pediatrician Matt Sabin from Melbourne, had a similarly exciting opportunity to offer. Could we help explore dietary data collected from children and adolescents to see whether protein leverage could explain obesity in these groups?

Thanks to Roger, we next met with a PhD student, Michelle Blumfield, and her supervisor Professor Clare Collins, a dietitian researcher from Newcastle. They told us of their Women and Their Children's Health (WATCH) study, into which 179 women had been enrolled during pregnancy. The research team had recorded the mothers' diets and health, and then the body composition of their newborn babies. The plan was to follow up the health of the children at four years of age.

We started by asking two questions: Could we see evidence for protein leverage in the mothers? And what was the effect of their diet on the baby's body composition?

Mothers' total energy intake (and BMI) rose as the percent of protein in their diet fell—exactly as predicted by protein leverage.

This was especially pronounced when the diets contained less than 16 percent protein and more than 40 percent fat.

When we mapped the body composition of the babies onto their mothers' diets, two patterns emerged. First, babies born to women whose diet contained less than 16 percent protein had steeply higher amounts of abdominal (belly) fat than did babies from mothers who had eaten a higher-protein diet. Second, levels of chubby baby fat (measured at the thigh) were highest when the mother's diet fell within a narrow band of protein content—from 18 to 20 percent. Higher than 20 percent protein, and babies were born increasingly lean—not necessarily a good thing; lower than 18 percent, and babies started to develop belly fat rather than chubby fat.

Chubby, subcutaneous baby fat, especially on the arms and legs, is a feature of healthy human infants. High amounts of abdominal fat, however, rang alarm bells. When the children were followed up at age four, the warning was louder still: there was evidence of elevated blood pressure in the children of women whose diet had been low in protein during pregnancy.

The message from Michelle and Clare's data was clear. During pregnancy, it would be advisable for women, both for their own health and that of their babies, to eat a diet containing 18 to 20 percent protein combined with healthy fats and carbs. Importantly, micronutrient intakes were best in mothers whose diets contained 18 to 20 percent protein along with low (30 percent) fat and high (50 percent) carbs. It appeared that mixing a diet with these macronutrient proportions required the women to eat a variety of plant-based and animal foods that, by correlation, had also included a healthy mix of vitamins and minerals that came along for the ride.

A newborn baby's culinary life involves little choice on their part—other than left breast or right. If nursed, they will receive a low-protein diet (about 7 percent) with 55 percent carbs (mainly lactose sugar) and 38 percent fat. That is the lowest-protein diet that any of us will ever consume, unless suffering famine. But it is unquestionably the optimal diet composition for an infant up to the time of weaning. This is true for all primates for an interesting reason: with our big brains and complex social lives, we need a long childhood so we can learn all we need to know as adults. Low-protein milk slows growth and makes this possible.

There's also a second reason mothers' milk is best: studies have shown that human babies raised on commercially available formula are more vulnerable to obesity later in life than those who are breast-fed. Many commercial milk formulations contain more protein than human breast milk. Experiments in which newborns were placed onto higher-protein formula (11 percent rather than 7 percent) have shown the same outcome—babies were at far greater risk of developing obesity over the first year of life, and as school-age children, and even as young adults. For this reason, the major producers of formula are now designing recipes with lower protein.

But why might a *high*-protein diet make babies fat later in life? Isn't this the opposite of what we found before—that *low*-protein ultraprocessed foods were linked to obesity?

No one knows the answer for sure. We think it may be because an unnaturally high-protein diet early in life sets the infant's protein target higher than it should be. And if an infant's protein target is set too high, they will someday have to eat more calories on a low-protein Western diet to reach their customary intake of protein. That is, of course, providing children also show powerful protein leverage in the same way as we adults do.

Matt Sabin, Christoph Saner, and their team at the Murdoch Children's Research Institute had collected data on children and adolescents with obesity who were enrolled in the COBRA study (Childhood Overweight BioRepository of Australia). When we helped analyze the results from their study, the conclusion was inescapable. The severity of childhood obesity was clearly associated with the relationship between protein and total calories consumed. Diluting protein in the diet was accompanied by increased calorie intake and higher BMI, just as we had found in adults. Children and adolescents show protein leverage.

That's not all. Kids and teenagers need ample protein and lots of energy to grow and be physically active. Every parent knows how hard it is to keep up with their children's apparently insatiable appetites. But spending too much time sitting at computer screens or video game monitors, coupled with increased consumption of low-protein, high-calorie ultraprocessed foods and beverages, is wreaking havoc on their health. It's made all the worse if the protein target is set too high in infancy.

As young adults, we still carry the imprint of our earlier life along with new burdens. The decade from twenty to thirty is when weight gain is becoming the most pronounced around the world. Leaving home, becoming independent, building a career, and establishing new relationships can all make it tough to stick to a healthy diet, a physically active lifestyle, and regular sleep patterns. Burning less energy in postadolescence means that we'll now need fewer fat and carb calories but the same target amount of protein. This can drive us to eat more than we need and create the conditions for obesity.

The health impacts of obesity in young men and women can even be felt across the generations by altering the expression of genes in the developing baby. We all bear the imprint of our parents' lifestyles, perhaps even those of our grandparents, through these so-called epigenetic marks. It is well known that the mother's egg transfers these marks to the biology of her baby, but there is growing evidence that even sperm may carry molecular messages that reflect a father's diet and are transmitted to the fertilized egg, setting his unborn child's health trajectory from birth. Whether these epigenetic marks set the newborn's protein target is not known, but if so, the implications are clear.

Pregnancy is a time when the mother's protein target rises by necessity to meet the demands of the growing fetus. Expectant mothers are advised to consume an extra 20 grams of protein each day (about a third more) during the second and third trimesters of pregnancy. Energy requirements also rise by around 350 kcal (about a fifth more). Achieving these higher needs translates into increasing the percent of protein in the diet by a bit—but not too much—while taking care not to overeat carbs and fats.

Once we move into middle age, roughly forty to sixty-five, diets that are lower in protein (10 to 15 percent), higher in carbs (but *healthy* carbs), and moderate in healthy fats will promote health and retard the process of aging. The emphasis on healthy carbs means high-fiber intake to slow gut emptying, increase feelings of fullness, and keep the microbiome well fed and our bowel healthy. Such a diet comprises moderate amounts of lean meat, poultry, eggs, fish, dairy, and nuts; copious vegetables, fruits, beans, and grains; and modest amounts of good fats, such as olive oil.

But then, into our twilight years, beyond sixty-five or so, there is once more a need for greater protein in the diet—more than in middle age. This is a consequence of our bodies becoming less efficient at retaining protein—the drain becomes increasingly leaky in old age. We now have an increased tendency to break down lean tissue protein and turn it into glucose in our livers, which is one reason muscle wastage is a feature of advanced age. Something like 18 to 20 percent protein is likely to help support these extra requirements but without excess calorie intake.

Intriguingly, we could see this exact pattern in our mice in Chapter 8. Colleague Alastair Senior showed that our mice suffered the greatest risk of dying on a high-protein, low-carb diet during middle age, but when very old, they benefited from a higher protein intake.

We have seen how the protein target changes from cradle to grave and how it can be set in early life, even before birth. We mention this because, if we are right about too-high protein targets leading to obesity, it can explain some very important things that are not yet understood, such as why indigenous populations, like the Amerindians, Australian Aboriginals and Torres Strait Islanders, New Zealand Maori, and other First Nations peoples, are particularly vulnerable to becoming obese on processed-food diets. Perhaps it's because they have recently switched from higher-protein, traditional diets. One population that fits this pattern particularly well is the Circumpolar Inuit. These people are among the most vulnerable of all populations to becoming obese when exposed to typical Western diets. They also, traditionally, have had a diet with the highest percentage of protein (more than 30 percent) of any population in recent history.

Here is an inescapable truth: the higher our protein target, the more food we must eat to get there. And when the foods are high in fats and carbs and low in fiber, the more energy we will eat. When we don't burn those extra calories, we pile on the pounds and risk becoming insulin resistant. Once that happens, we are stuck in a vicious cycle driven by our protein appetite, pushing us toward continuous weight gain in our current obesogenic food environment. How, then, can we escape?

CHAPTER 13 AT A GLANCE

1. Our needs for protein and energy change with lifestyle and across our lives, from birth to old age. Our protein target may even be set before we are born by the lifestyles of our parents.
2. The higher our protein target, the more food we must eat to get there. When the diet is low in fiber and high in energy, this means consuming extra calories to reach the protein

target; this increases our risk of becoming overweight and insulin resistant (prediabetic).

3. Insulin resistance increases the rate of loss of body protein, causing the protein target to rise further, promoting a vicious cycle that drives overeating, continuing weight gain, and development of type 2 diabetes, heart disease, and other health issues.
4. How can we escape this vicious cycle?

14

Putting Lessons into Practice

"Everything should be made as simple as possible," Albert Einstein wrote, "but not simpler." This is the approach we've tried to take, throughout all our efforts, to understand nutrition.

The first step in our scientific journey, our research into locust feeding, challenged an oversimplified view held by many—that animals have a single appetite that drives all of their intake. We learned that things are more complex than that; and to tame this complexity, we invented a new concept, a way of understanding why and how we eat, called *Nutritional Geometry*.

But what could *geometry* have to do with eating? We used it to explore and visualize the interrelationships among the appetites locusts have, each for a different nutrient. Ultimately, we were able to show that of all the appetites, that for protein has the strongest, but not the only, influence on intake. Locusts, we saw, try their best to get just the right amount of protein to support healthy development—neither too little nor too much.

That realization provided one of the key insights of this book and one that has guided us ever since: the strong appetite for protein shared by most animals can lead them to eat too much or too little of *other* nutrients, including fats and carbs. If their protein appetite is not satisfied, they will overeat. Once they get enough protein, their appetites cease driving them to eat more.

That's as simple as we can make nutrition—without oversimplifying it.

This set us up to tackle the biggest challenge of all. Can this view help us understand why nutrition has gone so wrong in the most complex species of all—ourselves? Could the same principles that apply to locusts in little plastic boxes hold true for us humans with our infinite choices of what to eat and how much?

Yes, it turns out. We traveled from mountains to islands to deserts and cities and studied species from slime molds and monkeys to crickets and college students. Our nutrition, we discovered, is no more complicated than that of our fellow living things. We, too, have a strong appetite for protein that determines what and how much we eat.

But dramatic changes in our food environment, particularly the displacement of traditional whole-food diets with ultraprocessed foods, have unbalanced our diets, causing us to overeat all the wrong things. The current global health crisis of obesity, diabetes, and heart disease is the direct result of that transformation of our food supply.

We owe a debt of gratitude to those humble locusts who taught us to think differently about nutrition and diets and set us off on a lifelong journey to apply this approach to examining the natural world—and then to ourselves.

And what is the significance for *you?* We hope that the lessons we've learned can help guide you toward healthy and sensible eating choices. To help, we have prepared a summary of our main points. We have also prepared a few examples to show how the lessons we've learned can be applied.

What We Know

1. A specific craving for protein is universal. This appetite has evolved to help all animals reach their target intake of the nutrient. When animals need protein, they experience a hunger for its flavor. When we humans are short of protein, the lip-smacking savory taste of umami becomes irresistible.
2. The protein appetite cooperates with a few other appetites—including those for carbs, fats, sodium, and calcium—to guide animals to a healthy, balanced diet.
3. This guidance system evolved in natural food environments, where reliable correlations existed between all the nutrients contained in foods, meaning that by regulating the intake of just those five nutrients, the rest of a balanced diet, containing dozens of other beneficial substances, came along for the ride.
4. But even in nature, there are times when certain foods become scarce, and it may not be possible to eat a balanced diet. Under these circumstances, appetites compete with one another rather than cooperate.
5. In humans and a variety of other species—but not all—protein wins this competition. As a result, the appetite for this nutrient determines our overall eating patterns.

6. If our food environment contains too little protein, we will overeat until we satisfy our protein appetite. If the proportion of protein is greater than our bodies require, the protein appetite will be satisfied sooner—when fewer total calories have been eaten.
7. This does not mean that more protein is better—far from it. Organisms from yeast cells to flies, mice, and monkeys have evolved *not* to overconsume protein for good reasons, mainly this one: eating too much protein switches on biological processes that hasten aging and shorten lives.
8. Our capacity to balance our nutrition has become seriously impaired due to the industrialization of the food system. We have:
   - made low-protein processed foods taste unnaturally good by adding sugars, fats, salt, and other chemicals;
   - diluted the presence of protein in the food supply with cheap and abundant ultraprocessed fats and carbs;
   - disconnected the brake on our appetite systems by decreasing our intake of fiber, which promotes fullness and feeds our gut bugs;
   - changed food cultures globally by aggressively marketing these products, including to kids, to establish them as the norm;
   - increased animal production unsustainably to meet the world's hunger for meat protein, with associated environmental harm; and
   - driven a decline in the protein content of our staple food plants by increasing the level of carbon dioxide in the atmosphere.

This list of points we find pretty alarming, to be honest. It shows that we have engineered ourselves a food environment that is incompatible with our nutritional biology. But the good news is that we now know enough to begin fixing the problems by working with rather than against our biology.

Let's start with Mary.

Mary's Story: A Tale with Two Outcomes

Mary is 45 years old. She's a mother with two teenage kids. She is moderately active, mainly as a by-product of running around juggling work, household, and family, although she took out a gym membership a year ago and tries to take a class every week. She worries about gaining weight and does her best to keep her BMI (body mass index) around 25, above which would be classified by medical professionals as overweight, like two-thirds of the adults in Australia, where she lives. Because Mary is 1.6 meters (5 feet 3 inches) tall and weighs 64 kilograms (141 pounds), she's presently spot-on at a BMI of 25. [You calculate BMI by dividing your weight in kilograms by the square of your height in meters. There are many online calculators if you prefer to use pounds and inches.]

What is Mary's protein target? There are various ways to estimate this, but let's use a simple one. We know that, for her age, a healthy diet for Mary should contain roughly 15 percent of total energy as protein. We can estimate her total daily calorie requirement with reasonable accuracy using an equation called the Harris Benedict formula, which estimates metabolic rate and is named after James Harris, an American botanist, and Francis Benedict, a chemist and physiologist, who published their method in 1919. There are various online calculators to help do this, based on your weight, height, sex, age, and how active you are. Plug in your numbers, and the formula will give you a reasonable estimate of your total energy needs—the number of calories you should eat daily to fuel your life and maintain your weight.

Based on the formula, Mary needs 1,880 kcal per day. If she consumes that daily, she will neither gain nor lose weight.

Fifteen percent of 1,880—the proportion recommended to come from protein—is 282 kcal. Because protein contains 4 kcal of energy per gram, this amounts to 70.5 grams (to be precise!) of the nutrient spread across the day. The remaining 1,600 kcal in Mary's diet will have to come from some combination of carbs and fats. We'll not worry about that for now.

What does 70.5 grams of protein look like? It can be found in any one of the following:

320 grams (11 ounces) of cooked lean meat or fish
680 grams (1 pound 8 ounces) of plain yogurt or cottage cheese
2,100 milliliters (71 fluid ounces) of fresh milk
850 grams (1 pound 14 ounces) of cooked kidney beans, lentils, or chickpeas
10 eggs
370 grams of nuts (13 ounces)
Or 1,400 grams (3 pounds) of doughnuts and fries (seriously)

Of course, these foods all contain more than protein. They also include some combination of carbs, fats, micronutrients, and fiber. This means that Mary would end up eating very different numbers of calories if she were to get her 70.5 grams of protein from, say, fish (she'd consume 580 kcal)—or donuts and fries (a whopping 5,500 kcal).

Therefore, she needs to get 70.5 grams of protein *and* no more than 1,880 kcal total over the course of a day.

It's been a hard few months, and Mary has drifted a little in her dietary habits. She's resorting to takeout a couple of nights each week. Her partner has been traveling and has not been around to help with afterschool pickup, food shopping, cooking, and housework. It's been a tough time at work, too, and she has had to drive farther each day through heavy traffic to a new client's office across town. By the time she gets home and deals with the aftermath of the day, cooking feels like the last thing she wants to do. And there's no fresh food in the refrigerator, anyhow—she hasn't been to the supermarket in five days.

After the pizza boxes are finally cleared away, school bags packed, and meeting papers read for tomorrow, Mary collapses in front of the TV, savors a glass of wine, and opens a bag of potato chips.

Despite her haphazard dietary and domestic circumstances, Mary's ancient and powerful protein appetite relentlessly ensures that she is eating her target 70.5 grams each day. But instead of her diet being 15 percent protein, the extra fat and carbs have slightly diluted it to 13 percent protein. Two percent doesn't sound like much of a difference, does it? Let's do the math:

On a 15 percent protein diet, Mary would eat 1,880 kcal a day, exactly what she'd need to remain at her present weight.

On her new 13 percent protein diet, Mary will eat 2,170 kcal in order to hit the same protein target—290 more kcal than she needs to stay at her current weight.

Let's put a face to that number: 290 kcal is equivalent to two cans of sugar-sweetened soda, or a chocolate bar, or a packet of potato chips. Again, doesn't sound like much, but unless she burns off these extra calories, Mary is likely to gain weight. If she stays on the 13 percent protein diet, in a couple of years she will have gained 12 kilograms (26 pounds), bringing her weight to 76 kilograms (167 pounds) and her BMI to 30, which is defined as obesity.

Where to next?

One Outcome

Mary's weight keeps rising slowly but steadily. By the time she reaches 76 kilograms (167 pounds), she'll need those 290 extra kcal she's been eating each day to remain at that higher weight. This is because a bigger body requires more fuel. Well, you'd think, at least she won't be gaining any *more* weight. But you'd be wrong. As we explained in the previous chapter, the leaky drain effect means that instead of remaining 12 kilograms (26 pounds) heavier than she started, Mary is now trapped in a vicious cycle driven by a growing appetite for protein. This virtually guarantees that she'll become even heavier.

Because of this vicious cycle, Mary has a rising protein target, and her appetite for this nutrient will relentlessly drive her to continue overeating. Due to all the highly processed foods and beverages in her diet, she is consuming less fiber than ever, which means the brakes on Mary's appetite are faulty. Her gut bugs will have started to notice the lack of fiber as well and will have begun to make their uncomfortable effects felt through constipation and irregular bowel movements.

Due to her increased weight, Mary's new target is 76 grams of protein; up a mere 5.5 grams from her previous target of 70.5 grams—literally an egg per day. Doesn't sound like much, but the consequences are dire.

On a 13 percent protein diet, Mary now needs to eat 2,340 kcal each day to get her 76 grams of protein. Because of these extra 168 kcal, she'll weigh 83 kilograms (183 pounds) before long, with a BMI of 32.4. And even that won't be the end of it: Mary's protein target will have risen even further with the progression of insulin resistance, driving her toward ever more serious health problems, including type 2 diabetes.

An Alternative Outcome

Mary has caught herself just in time to prevent further weight gain. All she needs to do is get back to a 15 percent protein diet, kick the junk food habit, and add some fiber. Her protein appetite will do the rest.

Importantly if counterintuitively, Mary *doesn't* need to eat more protein-rich foods to do this. By removing just 290 kcal of fats and carbs, she will increase the percentage of protein in her diet from 13 to a healthy 15 percent. She'll reach her 70.5 grams protein target, having eaten fewer calories than before, and her weight will drift back toward 64 kilograms (141 pounds). Cutting out one bag of chips on the couch will do it, as will skipping those two sodas or beers, or that chocolate bar. A few extra servings of fruit and veggies, beans, or whole grains would deal with the fiber issues, while also adding essential micronutrients and healthy phytochemicals. (Whole grains include all parts of the seeds of cereals such as wheat, spelt, rye, oats, barley, millet, and rice. Refined grains include only the starchy parts of the seed, with the fiber-containing bran and nutrient-rich germ removed.)

If Mary went harder and cut out 510 fat and carb calories, she'd be all the way up to a 17 percent protein diet, and would only need to eat 1,660 kcal to reach her protein target. This would be 150 or so fewer kcal than she needs to maintain her weight at 66 kilograms (146 pounds). She could do this by cutting out two of her favorites: a bag of chips, a chocolate bar, a couple of cans of soda, beer, or glasses of wine. Again, there is no need to eat more protein—the target remains the same at 70.5 grams, so it is a matter of how many calories of other stuff Mary needs to eat to get there.

And let's not forget that she could also increase her levels of physical activity to burn some extra calories and improve her general health.

Mary is pretty much every middle-aged woman or man living in the developed world. Her issues afflict us all, but her solutions can also be ours.

Once Mary reaches her older years, sixty-five and above, she will need to start increasing her protein intake a little, by around 25 grams per day, to a 20 percent protein diet. This is for the reasons we explained in the previous chapter: the protein drain becomes more leaky with old age, and unless Mary increases her intake, she risks losing muscle mass.

Matthew's Story

Matthew is twenty-five years old. He moved away from home after finishing college a year ago and is working full-time in an office in a new city. The hours are long, and he's expected to be there late most evenings. Cooking has never been his thing, and online deliveries are so easy. In his late teens, Matthew was a talented football player and trained hard to build bulk. Over three years he beefed up from a gangly beanpole to a muscular kid weighing 85 kilograms (187 pounds). He drove his parents to distraction with his blended protein shakes and eggs and multipacks of chicken breasts that cluttered the family refrigerator, but those days have gone. His football days are also over and with them his intense training regime.

During his life as an athlete, Matthew was eating around 135 grams of protein each day, which he needed to build and maintain his ample muscle mass. He was also expending 3,550 kcal of energy daily, needed to fuel his high level of physical activity. Now, he sits in front of a computer screen all day at work and is burning only 2,550 kcal each day. His muscle mass is starting to waste away without football and weight training—if you don't use it, you lose it—but it's still making its demands felt through his protein appetite.

At the end of his athletic career, Matthew could hit the bull's-eye for both protein and energy if he stuck to a 15 percent protein diet (eating 135 grams of protein would mean eating 3,600 kcal).

The problem today is that he now needs 1,000 fewer calories a day. To eat that amount on a 15 percent protein diet would provide Matthew with just 95 grams of protein per day. His protein target, still for now set high, courtesy of his sporting days, will remain unsatisfied, urging him to keep eating.

It will take time for Matthew's protein target to reset to a lower level more suited to his new sedentary lifestyle. How long, we don't know. The science remains to be done, but by then Matthew's waistline will be showing the effects of the accumulated excess calories he will have eaten chasing a high-protein target set during athletic training. Matthew will be following a trend seen among many fit young people as they enter their twenties and thirties, planting the seeds for chronic health problems in his forties and fifties.

What should Matthew do? To avoid weight gain, he needs to limit his calorie intake to 2,550 kcal, while also satisfying his ravenous protein appetite, with its higher-than-necessary demand for 135 grams of protein each day. To do that, he'll simply need to increase the percent of protein in his diet from 15 to 21 percent. That way, he'll hit his protein target (135 grams) and his energy needs (2,550 kcal) at the same time. Cutting out ultraprocessed foods and upping fiber intake are simple ways to help concentrate protein in his diet up to 21 percent, but increasing the portion sizes of protein-rich foods to add an extra 20 to 30 grams of protein each day to his diet would also help him get there.

Simple.

It has hardly been true for most of the time our species has existed, but today, losing a bit of weight is a goal many of us share. Losing it is tough enough, but keeping it off is harder still. The yo-yo effect is all too common—lose weight by going on the latest fad diet, bounce back to the previous weight, or even worse, put on more.

It's a terrific business model for the weight-loss industry, and the combination of our biology and modern food environment makes it near inevitable.

Working with protein leverage can help, as we saw with Mary and Matthew. There is evidence from large-scale clinical trials, such as the European DIOGENES study, that a higher-protein diet (25 percent) coupled with lots of healthy, slowly digested carbs helps keep weight off after a period on a low-calorie diet (800 kcal per day for 8 weeks in the case of that particular study).

However, a common rookie error is to look at the health benefits of a higher-protein diet and credit protein itself. Here's how the flawed logic goes: you lose weight on a high-protein diet; upon losing weight, your health improves; therefore, protein improves our health. But protein isn't a medicine for fixing diabetes, heart disease, and the other complications of obesity. As we now know, eating a diet with a high concentration of protein simply provides a limit on total calorie intake. Every other benefit follows from that.

But today, there is a fad diet community that believes "if some protein is good, more must be better." Another common error of logic. It's as false as saying that more of *any* good thing should be better than precisely the right amount. There are plenty of beneficial substances—salt, water, vitamins—that are toxic at too-high levels. The same is true for protein, as well as carbohydrates and fats.

The high-protein dietary philosophy has been in vogue for some time now. It was popularized in the works of Robert Atkins, who recommended a low-carb, high-fat, high-protein diet to achieve weight loss. He was right, and now we all know why—on such a diet, you eat less overall because you have focused on fulfilling the protein appetite. In the wake of Atkins came the popularity of paleo, ketogenic, carnivory, other low-carb and even zero-carb diets that advise eating nothing but meat, fish, eggs, butter (and maybe a little fiber among the more cautious) for effortless weight control and robust, animal good health.

Without fail, these will all stimulate weight loss. Added to the hunger-busting effects of protein, the very low-carb keto regimen (on which you'd eat less than 20 grams of carbs—the equivalent of an apple a day) causes the body to burn ketones, which are breakdown products of fat, as the main cellular fuel, rather than glucose. Ketones also seem to help curb calorie intake even when protein levels are modest.

Low-protein (9 percent), very high-fat (90 percent) keto diets are therapeutic in certain circumstances, such as for the treatment of epilepsy in children; and very low-carb, low-energy diets can help reverse the symptoms of type 2 diabetes; but neither is sustainable nor desirable for most of us as a regular diet. Even somewhat less extreme low-carb, high-fat diets have low compliance—most of us soon drift back to a more balanced mixture of macronutrients.

The reason is simple—if you remove most carbs from the diet, you activate the carbohydrate appetite, which will make starchy and sweet foods fabulously desirable. Try cutting carbs for a few days and see. If your diet is also low in protein, then you will get the double whammy of protein *and* carb cravings, along with the increasing desire never to see fat again, as your appetite for that nutrient tells you to stop eating it. Your appetites are simply doing what they have evolved to do—trying their best to guide you to a balanced diet.

If you persist on a low-carb (or any extreme) diet, against all the urges to do otherwise, your body will eventually adapt to it. We are an extraordinarily flexible creature when it comes to diet. It's been a hallmark of our success as a species that we've been able to adapt to diets as unpromising as those of the traditional Inuit (based on fish and the meat and blubber of mammals), the Masai of Kenya (milk and blood), or the Okinawans' low-protein, sweet potato–based fare.

There is a downside, however—the more you restrict your nutrient choices, the more you risk losing metabolic flexibility and will find it difficult to shift to a different dietary pattern. This is because our biology evolved to expect a variety of foods across the seasons, to fast overnight, and to experience times of feasting and famine. Physiologically, we are like athletes who need to stretch their muscles and tendons to maintain the ability to respond flexibly to whatever challenge is thrown at them. Unless we keep our physiology "stretched," we will gradually lose the ability to enjoy a healthy variety of diets.

Now, there is no doubt that weight loss can be a good thing for health and lifespan—*if* you are above a healthy weight and especially when there are signs of diabetes and cardiovascular disease. Its benefits for improving all manner of markers of poor health associated with obesity are legion.

But knowing what we now know about the molecular mechanisms of longevity, a high-protein, low-carb, high-fat diet poses a potential risk of its own. Our experiments with insects and mice, supported by research by other scientists around the world, show that such diets activate ancient and universal biochemical pathways that stimulate growth and reproduction. But at the same time, they switch *off* the repair and maintenance pathways that help support a long and healthy life.

Is there evidence that such risks are real in humans? There is a growing body of evidence, but studies have yet to run long enough to say for sure. For obvious reasons, we can't run highly controlled lifelong experiments on human nutrition the way we can with insects and rodents. Interpreting the results from short-term dietary trials in humans and from nutritional surveys is fraught with difficulties. Conclusions are often disputed by the proponents of different dietary camps, who usually have a single-nutrient focus, commonly squabbling over the relative roles of fats versus carbs.

Still, it's undeniable that we humans share the same basic molecular biology as yeast, worms, flies, mice, and monkeys when it comes to the longevity and growth pathways. This leaves us with a question: What are the odds that our species is a rare exception to the rule that long-term exposure to a high-protein, low-carb diet is life-shortening? Pretty low, we think. Vanishingly so. Especially when you consider that the longest-lived, healthiest populations on the planet are those who consume a lower-protein, high-carb whole-food diet.

Final Take-Home Tips: How to Eat Like the Animals

Mary and Matthew have helped put into practice some of the important messages from the book—lessons learned from creatures spanning blobs to baboons, locusts to cannibal crickets, fruit flies to mice, cats, dogs, and primates. All of them are part of the same wondrous evolutionary journey that includes us, an animal that has managed to change its world to meet its ancestral heart's desire for endless tasty, convenient, cheap food. With disastrous consequences. We need to take back our nutrition and work with, not outsmart, our biology.

Let's end our journey with some tips for taking charge of your food environment and helping your appetites work for you. This is not a prescription for how to live your life but rather our take on the scientific evidence as informed by our own research. It's a road map for your journey toward a healthy and enjoyable diet.

1. Estimate your protein target in three steps:

Step 1. Estimate the daily energy (calorie) requirement for your age, sex, and level of activity. You can do this by using something called the Harris Benedict equation calculator, available online at numerous websites.

Step 2. Estimate the portion of those calories that should come as protein (i.e., your protein intake target) by multiplying that value by:

Child and adolescent: 0.15 (i.e., a 15 percent protein diet)
Young adult (18–30): 0.18
Pregnant and breastfeeding: 0.20
Mature adult (30s): 0.17
Middle years (40–65): 0.15
Older age (>65): 0.20

Step 3. Divide that number by 4 to get the number of grams of protein per day you should eat, remembering that each gram of protein contains 4 kcal of energy.

2. Avoid ultraprocessed foods. Keep them out of the house. You will eat them if they are there. They exist to be irresistible. These are the number-one culprit in the global crisis of chronic disease—they have perverted the interplay between nutrients and appetites. How to recognize them? Here's how, in the words of Carlos Monteiro himself:

> A practical way to identify an ultra-processed product is to check to see if its list of ingredients contains at least one item characteristic of the NOVA ultra-processed food group, which is to say, either food substances never or rarely used in kitchens (such as high-fructose corn syrup, hydrogenated or interesterified oils, and hydrolysed proteins), or classes of additives designed to make the final product palatable or more appealing (such as flavours, flavour enhancers, colours, emulsifiers, emulsifying salts, sweeteners, thickeners, and anti-foaming, bulking, carbonating, foaming, gelling and glazing agents).

3. Choose high-protein foods from a variety of animal (poultry, meat, fish, eggs, and dairy) and/or plant (seeds, nuts, legumes) sources to both reach your intake target and ensure a balanced ratio of amino acids, which will satisfy the protein appetite most effectively. If you are vegetarian, which is no bad thing, you will need to make

greater efforts to eat a variety of foods, given that single plant proteins tend to be less well balanced in their amino acid content than many animal-derived proteins.

To help get a feel for how to reach your protein target, our dietitian colleague at the Charles Perkins Centre, Dr. Amanda Grech, has provided the following lists of foods, with their protein contents along with fat, carbs, kcal, saturated fat, and sodium.

Mean nutrient composition per 100g (3.5 oz)

Major Food Groups	(n)	Proportion of protein*	Proportion of energy^	Energy (kcal)	Protein (g)	Protein (%E)	Carbohydrate (g)	Dietary fiber (g)	Total fat (g)	Total saturated fatty acids (g)	Sodium (mg)
Milk, yogurt, and cheese and dairy-based discretionary	14784	12.9	10.9	89.2	4.0	17.8	8.7	0.2	4.4	2.4	96.3
Red meat, chicken, and seafood	12142	40.4	18.3	194.9	16.2	33.2	8.8	0.6	10.3	3.1	515.0
Eggs	2036	4.1	2.4	185.4	12.1	26.1	3.3	0.1	13.5	4.3	433.8
Beans, legumes, nuts, and seeds	3183	4.0	3.7	231.2	9.5	16.4	21.6	5.5	13.1	2.2	344.3
Breads, grains, cakes, crackers, rice, cereals, pasta/rice/corn dishes	25213	30.6	38.9	230.2	6.8	11.9	32.2	2.2	8.4	2.8	396.3
Fruits	9766	1.4	4.8	56.8	0.6	4.3	13.5	1.3	0.5	0.1	4.6
Vegetables	15424	4.0	7.1	106.4	2.3	8.5	14.7	2.0	4.8	1.1	257.9
Condiments	3182	0.1	1.5	452.0	1.0	0.9	6.9	0.1	47.0	12.1	795.8
Confectionary and alcoholic/nonalcoholic beverages	34703	2.5	12.5	14.6	0.1	3.0	2.8	0.0	0.1	0.0	6.6
Total	**120433**	100.0	100.0								

*Proportion each food group contributes to protein in the US diet
^Proportion each food group contributes to energy in the US diet
(n) = number of times food group was reported by participants
%E = percentage energy as protein

Mean nutrient composition^ per 100 g (3.5 oz) of food groups and selected foods reported by participants in NHANES 2015–2016*

		Nutrients (per 100g/3.5 oz)							
Food groups and selected foods	**(n)**	**Energy (kcal)**	**Protein (g)**	**Protein (%E)**	**Carbohydrate (g)**	**Dietary fiber (g)**	**Total fat (g)**	**Saturated fatty acids (g)**	**Sodium (mg)**
Dairy products and dishes	14784	89.2	4.0	17.8	8.7	0.2	4.4	2.4	96
– Plain milk	4822	51.9	3.3	25.1	4.8	0.0	2.2	1.3	45
– Strawberry milk, whole	19	81.3	3.0	14.6	10.6	0.0	3.1	1.7	43
– Plain Greek yogurt, nonfat	11	59.0	10.2	69.1	3.6	0.0	0.4	0.1	36
– Yogurt, whole fat, fruit flavored	26	86.9	3.1	14.3	12.4	0.1	2.9	1.8	44
– Heavy cream	5	340.0	2.8	3.3	2.7	0.0	36.1	23.0	26
Cheese	1580	362.2	24.0	26.5	4.1	0.0	27.7	16.3	744
– Brie	11	332.3	20.8	25.0	0.4	0.0	27.7	17.4	631
– Cheddar	465	404.8	22.9	22.6	3.1	0.0	33.3	18.9	653
Processed/American cheese	861	297.5	15.9	21.4	8.7	0.0	22.3	12.7	1253
Ice cream	1157	215.3	3.7	6.9	26.1	0.7	10.9	6.3	84
– Rich chocolate ice cream, with a thick chocolate coating	4	302.8	5.6	7.4	11.9	1.1	25.8	15.9	56
Meat, chicken, and seafood products and dishes	12142	194.9	16.2	33.2	8.8	0.6	10.3	3.1	515
Beef	933	225.2	27.7	49.3	0.9	0.1	11.7	4.6	431
– Beef, roast, roasted, fat not eaten	35	149.8	29.1	77.8	0.0	0.0	3.7	1.4	417
– Pork chop, fat eaten	18	211.3	27.7	52.4	0.0	0.0	10.5	3.3	514
Processed Meats—sausages, hot dogs, salami	1984	218.7	16.2	29.6	2.4	0.0	15.8	5.4	970
Chicken	2678	229.6	21.6	37.6	7.0	0.4	12.5	2.8	507
– Chicken breast, grilled, without skin	63	175.6	29.6	67.5	0.0	0.0	5.5	1.0	353
– Chicken drumstick, coated, fried, fast food	32	292.8	16.2	22.2	12.9	0.4	19.6	4.6	748
Fish	261	178.2	21.4	48.1	4.0	0.2	8.1	1.6	467

Food groups and selected foods	(n)	Energy (kcal)	Protein (g)	Protein (%E)	Carbohydrate (g)	Dietary fiber (g)	Total fat (g)	Saturated fatty acids (g)	Sodium (mg)
Burgers and sandwiches with meat	1525	262.0	13.3	20.3	22.0	1.2	13.3	4.8	568
– Cheeseburger	57	270.3	13.5	20.0	25.5	1.9	12.9	5.8	628
– Chicken sandwich, whole-wheat bread, salad	3	203.5	16.2	31.8	19.6	3.0	7.0	1.3	364
Eggs and egg dishes	**2036**	185.4	12.1	26.1	3.3	0.1	13.5	4.3	434
Eggs, whole, yolk, or white	863	184.4	13.2	28.5	0.9	0.0	13.8	4.3	442
Beans, legumes, nuts, and seeds products and dishes	**3183**	231.2	9.5	16.4	21.6	5.5	13.1	2.2	344
Beans and bean dishes	411	166.8	8.4	20.3	23.6	8.1	4.7	0.7	228
– Black beans, cooked	8	133.6	8.9	26.6	24.3	10.1	0.4	0.1	348
Legumes and legume dishes	110	193.3	9.1	18.9	24.9	7.5	6.9	1.1	252
– Lentils, cooked	20	115.5	9.0	31.1	20.0	7.9	0.4	0.1	196
Seeds	23	576.3	19.1	13.3	23.8	11.0	49.2	5.2	462
Nuts	744	598.3	18.8	12.6	22.0	8.2	52.9	7.1	175
Peanut butter	308	580.4	21.5	14.8	23.0	5.1	49.0	9.7	431
Grains and grain-based products and dishes	**25213**	230.2	6.8	11.9	32.2	2.2	8.4	2.8	396
Bread, wheat or cracked wheat, whole wheat	1401	270.7	11.0	16.3	47.0	5.1	4.4	0.9	472
Bread, croissants, bagels, English muffins, rolls	2985	303.8	9.1	12.0	50.6	2.4	7.0	2.2	494
Quinoa, cooked	19	119.9	4.4	14.6	21.2	2.8	1.9	0.2	163
Pasta, cooked	17	148.2	6.0	16.1	29.9	3.9	1.7	0.2	235
Rice, white, boiled	570	129.2	2.7	8.3	28.0	0.4	0.3	0.1	245.3
Rice, brown, boiled	110	122.4	2.7	8.9	25.4	1.6	1.0	0.3	202.2
Breakfast cereals	2345	374.8	7.7	8.2	80.8	6.3	4.3	1.0	436
– Froot Loops	122	375.8	5.3	5.6	88.0	9.3	3.4	1.8	470
– Bran Cereal	2	258.9	13.1	20.3	74.2	29.3	4.9	1.1	258
Pizza—fast food with cheese	3	266.2	11.4	17.1	33.3	2.3	9.7	4.5	598
Nachos with cheese, meat, and sour cream	5	215.5	6.3	11.7	20.1	3.4	12.6	3.1	323

Food groups and selected foods	(n)	Energy (kcal)	Protein (g)	Protein (%E)	Carbohydrate (g)	Dietary fiber (g)	Total fat (g)	Saturated fatty acids (g)	Sodium (mg)
Whole-wheat pasta with tomato-based sauce and seafood	4	108.0	5.7	21.0	18.8	2.8	1.7	0.2	217
Grain-based snack foods (e.g., popcorn, corn chips)	2220	497.6	7.8	6.2	62.2	5.2	24.8	5.7	714
Cakes	681	367.5	3.9	4.2	51.2	1.2	17.3	5.1	341
Cookies	2020	462.0	5.3	4.6	67.4	2.2	20.1	7.0	340
Breakfast pastries	528	407.2	5.3	5.2	53.0	1.8	19.6	7.6	358
Fruit products and dishes	9766	56.8	0.6	4.3	13.5	1.3	0.5	0.1	5
Fresh fruit	5692	67.3	0.8	4.6	15.1	2.3	1.2	0.2	8
Fruit juices	1316	49.0	0.2	1.9	12.0	0.3	0.1	0.0	5
Dried fruit	249	301.6	2.2	2.9	75.8	5.2	2.4	1.5	10
Vegetable products and dishes	**15424**	106.4	2.3	8.5	14.7	2.0	4.8	1.1	258
Fried potatoes	3947	313.9	3.9	5.0	37.2	2.9	17.6	2.9	360
Potato, boiled	9	92.6	2.5	10.8	21.1	2.2	0.1	0.0	164.5
Sweet potato, boiled	6	94.8	2.1	8.9	21.8	3.5	0.1	0.1	182.2
Carrot, raw	454	40.4	0.9	9.2	9.6	2.8	0.2	0.0	68.7
Leafy and dark greens	554	31.2	2.6	33.8	4.5	2.7	1.0	0.2	141
Green, string beans	10	30.8	1.8	23.8	7.0	2.7	0.2	0.1	6.3
Tomato, raw	1037	17.9	0.9	19.7	3.9	1.2	0.2	0.0	5
Confectionery	2219	441.2	3.7	3.3	77.2	1.5	13.8	7.4	119
Soft drinks	4129	33.7	0.0	0.4	8.4	0.0	0.1	0.0	7
Wine/beer/spirits	1385	81.4	0.2	1.2	3.9	0.0	0.1	0.0	12

^USDA Standard reference nutrient composition database (Legacy SR), for Food and Nutrient Database for Dietary Studies (FNDDS)

(n)=number of times food group was reported by participants

%E=percentage energy as protein

* The National Health and Nutrition Examination Survey (NHANES) assesses the health and nutritional status of adults and children in the United States. The survey is conducted continuously and includes approximately 5,000 adults and children each year. During the 2015–2016 collection period, 15,327 persons from 30 different locations across the U.S. were randomly selected to participate in the survey. Of those selected, 9,971 provided information on their diet.

4. Our physiologies evolved at a time when we ate a lot more fiber than we do today, which is why we rely on the presence of it in our diet to work alongside our appetites to control what we eat. Reconnect the appetite brake by including lots of leafy greens, non-starchy vegetables, fruits, seeds, and whole grains to ensure fiber without calorie load. Beans, seeds, and pulses (e.g., butter beans, kidney beans, chickpeas, black-eyed peas, lentils) also add fiber, protein, and healthy carbs. As a bonus, vitamins and minerals will come along for the ride, reducing the need for supplements.

5. Don't obsess about counting calories—get your diet right, and your protein appetite will manage the calories for you. Accompany the high-protein foods with lots of vegetables and fruits, beans, and whole grains, which will contain good carbs and fats. That way you will also satisfy your appetites for all three macronutrients at the same time.

6. Be restrained when adding sugar and salt to food, and choose healthy added fats, such as extra-virgin olive oil.

7. Doing all of the above only provides an estimate of your protein target and total energy needs—a starting point. Try adjusting up and down until you feel in control of your appetites—hungry by mealtimes and satisfied after and between meals.

8. Listen to your appetites. Ask yourself, "Am I craving salty, umami flavors?" If so, your body is telling you that you need protein. At such times you will be especially susceptible to the lure of protein decoys, such as ultraprocessed savory snack foods. Don't be seduced—seek out high-quality protein foods instead.

9. The flip side to the above is: don't eat more protein than you feel you want. Your protein appetite will get it right, and there is a

downside to eating too much of it. Our appetites are better gauges than our calculators.

10. When exercising and building muscle mass, the science suggests that eating 20 to 30 grams of protein within a meal best activates the cellular machinery for building new muscle proteins. That is the optimal dose of protein to kick-start muscle synthesis into action. The machinery involved in protein synthesis is the growth pathway that we discussed in Chapter 8, which, as an inevitable by-product, also produces cellular garbage and causes damage to cells and DNA. A meal containing 20 to 30 grams of protein will switch on protein synthesis for around 2 hours, limiting the side effects of protein synthesis to those periods within the day.

11. To help boost cellular and DNA repair and maintenance, fast overnight and limit snacking between main meals. For example, avoid eating after about 8pm until breakfast the next morning. This regular daily fast will help activate the longevity pathway (also introduced in Chapter 8), as well as reduce the risk that you will eat extraneous calories later in the evening, and assist with sleep.

There are various weight-loss programs that involve periods of restricted calorie intake (the 5:2 Fast Diet is one of the more popular), but the science is showing that even without eating fewer calories in total, there are health benefits from simply restricting the number of hours in the day when we eat (called "intermittent fasting" or "time-restricted feeding"). These benefits arise because a period of several hours without food turns off the damage-producing growth pathways and activates the cellular and DNA repair and maintenance processes that support health and longevity.

We can't eat when we're asleep. This means that nighttime sleep provides an opportunity to clear out the accumulated cellular garbage and repair the damage done to our DNA and tissues during the day. That much is true for all the cells in our bodies but especially so for our brain cells. No wonder, then, that time-restricted feeding and good sleep have both been linked to improved physical as well as mental health.

12. Sleep well. Sleep is the third pillar of health and wellness, along with diet and exercise. Sleep and nutrition are linked through the circadian body clock system.

Our biology is governed by a master clock, which sits in the brain. It runs on a twenty-four-hour cycle and controls daily rhythms of sleep-wakefulness, body temperature, gut emptying, blood pressure, insulin sensitivity, and much more. The master clock uses hormones such as melatonin to synchronize a multitude of separate mini clocks that are found in each of our organs. Indeed, every cell has its own private circadian clock, which is tightly linked to fundamental cellular processes like DNA replication and insulin signaling. Mess up the synchronization of these cellular and organ clocks, and you end up feeling terrible, as anyone who has suffered jet lag will know. Also, the risks of obesity, diabetes, cardiovascular disease, and cancer are all higher in long-term shift workers.

The master body clock doesn't run as accurately as a digital wristwatch, however. It runs a little slow, so each day it needs to be reset by a reliable environmental cue. The main clock-setting cue is daylight, but the timing of eating is also important. If you subject yourself to bright light or eat when your body clock is expecting you to be asleep, you'll end up with a scrambled clock system and, ultimately, with poor health outcomes.

13. Get active—outdoors if possible—and sociable. Physical activity and social interactions are clearly related to improved health and longevity.

14. Learn how to cook the foods you love—and then teach your children. This is among the greatest gifts you can give them.

15. Eat the foods you like (while minimizing ultraprocessed foods). There are endless ways to achieve a nutritionally balanced diet. Unless there are specific medical reasons, you don't need to cut out any food group (grains, dairy, or whatever) or eat things that you don't like or that are not appropriate to your food culture. The world's traditional and emerging food cultures are deeply connected to place, history, and religion and sustain people from cradle to grave, in sickness and in health. The various nutritional philosophies slugging it out today—from vegan to keto—can provide healthy eating in specific circumstances, but they are not sustainable for most of us and have been deeply infected by financial vested interests, anger, and zealotry.

So, that's it, our story is done. We have told you what the animals have told us about healthy eating. Except for one thing. There are many numbers, formulas, and scientific facts in the paragraphs and lists above. These can and should be important guides to a healthy lifestyle. But they should not be mistaken *for* a healthy lifestyle. Rather, use the knowledge and insights you have gained from this book as you might use a map on any journey—as a guide to get you there and for occasional reference if you lose your way.

Before long, eating an enjoyable healthy diet will become automatic, requiring little more than steering toward healthy food environments (and away from unhealthy ones) and listening to your appetites. It's like learning to play a sport or a musical instrument, or to drive an automobile: at first it takes concentration, consciously applying rules, rehearsing them, and unlearning bad habits. And then it becomes second nature.

Or, in the case of healthy diets, perhaps we should consider this *first* nature: creatures from slime molds to baboons have been doing it for millions of years before numbers, formulas, sports, music, and automobiles were even invented.

More on Nutrients

Protein

Proteins are molecules made up of chains of amino acid building blocks and are fundamental to the structure and function of plant and animal cells.

They are built from carbon, hydrogen, and oxygen, like the other macronutrients, but also contain essential nitrogen atoms.

Foods that are rich in protein include meat, poultry, seafood, dairy, eggs, beans, nuts, and pulses. Grains and vegetables contain smaller amounts of protein.

Amino acids

There are twenty common types of amino acids: alanine, arginine, asparagine, aspartic acid, cysteine, glutamine, glutamic acid, glycine, histidine, isoleucine, leucine, lysine, methionine, phenylalanine, proline, serine, threonine, tryptophan, tyrosine, and valine.

Leucine, isoleucine, and valine comprise the branched-chain amino acids, which are potent stimulators of muscle growth and are found in highest amounts in animal proteins (meat and dairy) and in some plant proteins, such as beans and pulses.

Proteins differ in their amino acid composition. The sequence of amino acids in a protein is coded by genes, which provide the blueprint for making proteins.

Obtaining a balanced mixture of amino acids in the diet requires eating a variety of different protein-rich foods.

Peptides

Peptides are shorter chains of amino acids than proteins, containing between two and fifty or so amino acids.

During digestion, the proteins we eat are broken down into small peptides (two or three amino acids) and amino acids for uptake across the gut.

We also make peptides in our bodies from amino acids, including many important hormones.

Carbohydrates ("Carbs")

Carbohydrates are sugars, starches, and fibers and are found in foods such as honey, fruits, vegetables, grains, beans, pulses, and milk. They also occur in low levels in liver and muscle meat in the form of glycogen (see below).

Carbohydrates are made up of carbon, hydrogen, and oxygen atoms in a 1:2:1 ratio.

Most carbs in nature are made from thin air and sunlight—by plants and algae using atmospheric carbon dioxide (CO_2) and water (H_2O) in the process of photosynthesis, at the same time releasing oxygen (O_2) into the atmosphere.

Sugars

Sugars are small carbohydrate molecules (saccharides). They are the building blocks of larger carb molecules, such as starch and fiber. The basic building blocks are the single "mono" saccharides, which include glucose, fructose (fruit sugar), and galactose (in milk).

Glucose is the primary product of photosynthesis by plants and algae. It is the main fuel for life for all organisms and is the blood sugar that circulates around our bodies.

One molecule of glucose joined to one molecule of fructose forms sucrose (a disaccharide)—which is table sugar (and what we normally call sugar). Sucrose circulates in the sap of plants, notably sugar cane.

High-fructose corn syrup is a sucrose substitute used in processed foods and beverages. It is a mixture of fructose and glucose, industrially produced by breaking down corn starch.

One molecule of glucose joined to one molecule of galactose forms lactose—milk sugar, the carb without which none of us would be here today.

Starch

Starch is a storage form of complex carbohydrate (polysaccharide), produced by plants by joining together long chains of smaller sugar units, mainly glucose. Starch is stored in tubers, stems, and seeds to provide the plant with energy for later germination and growth.

Starchy foods include breads, pasta, potatoes, and sweet potatoes.

Resistant starches are those that are difficult to digest without the assistance of microbes in the gut, which ferment them to produce short-chain fatty acids. Resistant starches are found in foods such as green bananas, beans, and lentils and are formed when starchy foods such as potatoes, pasta, and rice are cooked and allowed to cool. They are very important for gut health.

Fiber

Fiber is another complex carbohydrate produced by plants in which the simple sugar units are joined together; but unlike starch, the units are hard to break apart during digestion.

Fiber is an essential part of a healthy diet and mostly comes from vegetables, fruits, grains, pulses, beans, nuts, and seeds.

Soluble fiber is the gloopy stuff found in fruits, vegetables, oats, barley, and legumes. It slows the rate of gut emptying, which helps you feel fuller. It also lowers bad cholesterol and supports blood glucose control.

Insoluble fiber is the rough stuff that adds physical bulk and absorbs water, creating a feeling of fullness and softening feces in the bowel. It is found in whole-grain breads and cereals, nuts, seeds, wheat bran, and the skin and pulp of fruit and vegetables.

The most abundant carbohydrate fiber on the planet is cellulose. Cellulose is built by plants from glucose units and forms the rigid walls that surround plant cells. Our (animal) cells are squishy bags with flexible membranes, but plants require more structural support to remain upright and withstand the elements, so their cells are all housed in cellulose shells, and their main structural parts (stems, trunks) are reinforced with fiber and wood.

Cellulose is among the hardest carbohydrate for animals to break down and is indigestible to humans. It adds physical bulk to the diet, however, and helps dilute calories. It is also useful for making paper and textiles.

Glycogen

Glycogen is composed of glucose units and is the storage form of carbohydrates used by animals. We only store around 1 kilogram (2.2 pounds) of glycogen in our bodies, mainly in the liver but also in muscles; once this is used up, we need to liberate energy from stored fat. Marathon runners know this point of transition in fuel use as "hitting the wall."

The main source of carbs in the diet of traditional Inuit is glycogen.

Lipids (Fats, Oils, and Sterols)

Lipids are built mostly from carbon and hydrogen atoms and are not soluble in water.

Fats are solid at room temperature (butter, lard, coconut fat), whereas oils (vegetable oils, fish oils) are liquid.

The main fats and oils in our diet are made up of a glycerol molecule attached to three fatty acid molecules. They are found in many foods, such as dairy, meat, seafood, vegetable oils, nuts, avocados, and olives.

Fats and oils are used as an efficient energy reserve by plants and animals. This is because they store twice the energy per gram weight as do carbohydrates, which also means they deliver twice the calories per gram when eaten.

Fatty acids

Fatty acid molecules have a tail of carbon atoms, the length of which is used to classify them into short-chain, medium-chain, long-chain, and very long-chain fatty acids.

Short-chain fatty acids include acetate in vinegar and a range of other sour-tasting compounds produced by bacterial fermentation, which occurs when microbes ferment complex carbohydrates in the bowel and during the production of fermented foods such as sauerkraut and kimchi.

When all the carbon atoms in the tail of a fatty acid are joined by single links (bonds), they are called *saturated fatty acids.*

If there are double bonds between any of the carbon atoms in the tail, the fatty acid is said to be *unsaturated.*

If there is just one double bond in the chain, they are *monounsaturated fatty acids,* and *polyunsaturated fatty acids* have two or more double bonds.

If a double bond in a polyunsaturated fatty acid occurs at the third-to-last carbon molecule in its tail, it is termed an *omega-3 fatty acid*; if at the sixth-to-last, it is an *omega-6 fatty acid.*

The optimal ratio of omega-6 to omega-3 fatty acids for good health is between 1:1 and 4:1, but this is rarely achieved in the modern Western diet, and values of 16:1 are typical. Rebalancing this ratio requires eating more omega-3-rich foods.

Oily fish (salmon, herring, mackerel) are the most widely available sources of omega-3 fatty acids, and walnuts, hemp, and flaxseeds are also good sources.

Monounsaturated, polyunsaturated, and saturated fats and oils

Fats containing high levels of monounsaturated fatty acids (e.g. olive oil) are among the healthiest fats.

Polyunsaturated fatty acids are found in high levels in corn, canola, and safflower oils and fish oils.

Saturated fatty acids are most abundant in dairy, lard, and many other animal fats, as well as some vegetable oils such as coconut and palm oils. Saturated animal fats are widely considered to be less healthy than unsaturated fats.

Saturated fatty acid molecules tend to clump and stack together at room temperature to form solids (e.g., butter, lard, and coconut fat), whereas unsaturated fat molecules tend to remain apart and form liquids, called oils (e.g., fish and most vegetable oils).

Trans fats

Trans fats are solid fats produced by chemically treating unsaturated oils to break double bonds and saturate some of the fat molecules. This helps them to stack, making them solid at room temperature.

Trans fats added to processed foods are dangerous to health. They were used to make margarine until banned and are still used in highly processed snack, packaged, and fast foods.

Trans fats are rare in nature, although small amounts are produced naturally by bacteria in the stomachs of ruminant animals such as cows, sheep, and goats and are found in meat and dairy products from these animals.

Interesterified fats

Like trans fats, these are artificial fats that have been industrially produced by altering the chemical structure of vegetable oils.

They are created by swapping or rearranging fatty acids in fat molecules to alter the melting point, improve shelf life, and change mouthfeel.

The health effects of interesterified fats are poorly understood, and there is no requirement for package labels to declare interesterified fat content of processed foods.

Cholesterol

Cholesterol is another type of lipid called a sterol. It is essential for building animal cell membranes and for making steroid hormones and vitamin D.

Plants contain phytosterols. Cholesterol is only found in animal-based foods.

Cholesterol is transported in the blood by being attached to two types of carrier molecules called low-density lipoproteins (LDL) and high-density lipoproteins (HDL). A high ratio of LDL (bad cholesterol) to HDL (good cholesterol) is associated with poor cardiovascular health.

Soluble fiber in the diet is associated with reduced LDL, although the precise mechanisms are not fully understood.

Digestion

Once we have eaten complex proteins, fats, and carbs, so-called macronutrients, we need to break them down into their smaller constituent units (amino acids, fatty acids, and monosaccharides) that can be absorbed by the gut and then are able to sustain life.

Complex carbs ultimately get broken down into monosaccharides. For starch, this process starts in the mouth, where starch-digesting enzymes in saliva (amylases) get to work, breaking starch down to glucose.

Disaccharides such as table sugar (sucrose) and milk sugar (lactose) are split into monosaccharides by enzymes in the small intestine; these monosaccharides are then absorbed into the bloodstream. Sucrose gets broken into glucose and fructose.

Much of the fructose we eat is converted into glucose in the intestine, while the rest enters the blood and is processed by the liver. High intakes can lead to buildup of liver fat.

A person who lacks the enzyme for breaking milk sugar (lactose) into glucose and galactose is "lactose intolerant." Originally, we humans lost the ability to digest lactose at the time of weaning, but about 5,000 years ago, populations in different parts of the world evolved the ability to digest lactose and drink milk later in life, allowing full nutritional advantage to be taken of domesticating dairy animals.

Depending on how difficult the carbs in a meal are to digest, they may be completely broken down and absorbed into the bloodstream by the time they get much past the start of the small intestine on their way to the large bowel.

More complex carbohydrates and other forms of dietary fiber that are harder to digest make it down to the bowel, where the microbiome breaks them down, liberating energy, short-chain fatty acids, vitamins—and gas—in the process.

Protein digestion begins in the stomach through the action of stomach acids and pepsin and continues as the food enters the start of the intestine (the duodenum), where protein-digesting enzymes enter from the pancreas. Single amino acids and very small peptides (composed of two or three amino acids) are absorbed into the cells of the small intestine to be transported into the bloodstream.

The pancreas also secretes fat-digesting enzymes into the small intestine, and fats are emulsified by bile, which is produced by the liver, stored in the gall bladder, and enters the small intestine. The resultant fatty acids and other lipid components released are absorbed into the cells of the small intestine and then enter the bloodstream.

"Essential" Nutrients

There are around one hundred nutrients that should be in the diet for optimal health and well-being. Some forty of these are classified by nutritionists as being "essential" for humans, which means that they cannot be made by our bodies but must be consumed in the diet if we are to survive.

These include: nine amino acids (phenylalanine, valine, threonine, tryptophan, methionine, leucine, isoleucine, lysine, and histidine), two fatty acids (alpha-linolenic acid and linoleic acid), thirteen vitamins [A, C, D, E, K, thiamine (B_1), riboflavin (B_2), niacin (B_3), pantothenic acid (B_5), B_6, biotin (B_7), folate (B_9), and B_{12}], and fifteen minerals (potassium, chlorine, sodium, calcium, phosphorus, magnesium, iron, zinc, manganese, copper, iodine, chromium, molybdenum, selenium, and cobalt).

Phytochemicals

Phytochemicals are chemicals produced by plants as protection against their natural enemies—herbivores and diseases. Some are deadly to humans, others taste bitter, and some can be beneficial to health.

Phytochemicals have been used as poisons, recreational drugs, and traditional medicines by humans (and other animals) for millennia. Since agriculture began, we have tended to breed them out of our major food crops.

Some examples of healthy phytochemicals include the *anthocyanins,* which are found in red, blue, and purple fruits and vegetables; *flavonoids,* which are found in onions, berries, parsley, green tea, citrus, bananas, red wine, and dark chocolate; *carotenoids,* found in yellow and orange vegetables; and *salicin,* which is found in willow tree bark and is the basic chemical in aspirin.

Some phytochemicals are heavily marketed as food supplements, often because of their antioxidant and anti-inflammatory properties. Evidence that these supplements actually work, however, is limited at best. Far better to get your phytochemicals by eating fruit and vegetables.

Acknowledgments

We would first like to thank the many colleagues and students who have shared our adventures in nutritional biology over three decades. We have mentioned only a small number by name in the book, but there are many others, past and present, for whose friendships and contributions we are grateful.

Thank you, too, to Margaret Allman-Farinelli, Lisa Bero, Jennie Brand-Miller, Corinne Caillaud, Stephen Corbett, Annika Felton, Olivier Galy, David Mayntz, Carlos Monteiro, Marion Nestle, Robert Roemer, Jessica Rothman, Lesley Simpson, Michele Swan, Lhendup Tharchen, Jacqueline Tonin, and Erin Vogel for commenting on sections of the manuscript; to Amanda Grech, Paul

Zongo, and Rosie Ribeiro for help with dietetics; and to Alistair Senior and Samantha Solon-Biet for help with preparing figures.

Thank you to our agent, Catherine Drayton; to Bill Tonelli for his rapier-sharp editorial eye (including the eloquent translation of "two-halves of bugger all"); to Deb Brody and her team at Houghton Mifflin Harcourt; to Myles Archibald and his team at HarperCollins; and to our Australian HarperCollins crew. It has been a blast.

And finally, special thanks to Jacqueline and Lesley and our families for their love, support, and forbearance.

Further Reading

Here we provide a list of peer-reviewed publications that accompany the studies featured in the text of the book. They are listed in order of appearance in the text.

Introduction

Johnson, C., D. Raubenheimer, J. M. Rothman, D. Clarke, and L. Swedell. "30 Days in the Life: Nutrient Balancing in a Wild Chacma Baboon," *PLoS ONE* 8, no. 7 (2013): e70383.

Dussutour, A., T. Latty, M. Beekman, and S. J. Simpson. "Amoeboid Organism Solves Complex Nutritional Challenges," *Proceedings of the National Academy of Sciences of the United States of America* 107, no. 10 (2010): 4607–11.

Chapter 1: The Day of the Locusts

Raubenheimer, D., and S. J. Simpson. "The Geometry of Compensatory Feeding in the Locust," *Animal Behaviour* 45, no. 5 (1993): 953–64.

Simpson, S. J., and G. A. Sword. "Locusts," *Current Biology* 18, no. 9 (2008): R364–66.

Simpson, S. J., E. Despland, B. F. Hägele, and T. Dodgson. "Gregarious Behaviour in Desert Locusts Is Evoked by Touching Their Back Legs," *Proceedings of the National Academy of Sciences of the United States of America* 98, no. 7 (2001): 3895–97.

Anstey, M. L., S. M. Rogers, S. R. Ott, M. Burrows, and S. J. Simpson. "Serotonin Mediates Behavioral Gregarization Underlying Swarm Formation in Desert Locusts," *Science* 323, no. 5914 (2009): 627–30.

Buhl, J., D. J. T. Sumpter, I. D. Couzin, J. J. Hale, E. Despland, E. R. Miller, and S. J. Simpson. "From Disorder to Order in Marching Locusts," *Science* 312, no. 5778 (June 2, 2006): 1402–06.

Simpson, S. J., G. A. Sword, P. D. Lorch, and I. D. Couzin. "Cannibal Crickets on a Forced March for Protein and Salt," *Proceedings of the National Academy of Sciences of the United States of America* 103, no. 11 (2006): 4152–56.

Chapter 2: Calories and Nutrients

Simpson, S. J., and D. Raubenheimer. *The Nature of Nutrition: A Unifying Framework from Animal Adaptation to Human Obesity*. Princeton, NJ: Princeton University Press, 2012.

Ludwig, D. S., W. C. Willett, J. S. Volek, and M. L. Neuhouser. "Dietary Fat: From Foe to Friend?" *Science* 362, no. 6416 (2018): 764–70.

Ludwig, D. S., F. B. Hu, L. Tappy, and J. Brand-Miller. "Dietary Carbohydrates: Role of Quality and Quantity in Chronic Disease," *BMJ* 361(2018): k2340.

Chapter 3: Picturing Nutrition

Raubenheimer, D., and S. J. Simpson. "The Geometry of Compensatory Feeding in the Locust," *Animal Behaviour* 45, no. 5 (1993): 953–64.

Simpson S. J., and D. Raubenheimer. "A Multi-Level Analysis of Feeding Behaviour: The Geometry of Nutritional Decisions," *Philosophical Transactions of the Royal Society B* 342, no. 1302 (1993): 381–402.

Raubenheimer, D., and S. J. Simpson. "Integrative Models of Nutrient Balancing: Application to Insects and Vertebrates," *Nutrition Research Reviews* 10, no. 1 (1997): 151–79.

Chapter 4: Dance of the Appetites

Simpson, S. J., S. James, M. S. J. Simmonds, and W. M. Blaney. "Variation in Chemosensitivity and the Control of Dietary Selection Behaviour in the Locust," *Appetite* 17, no. 2 (October 1991): 141–54.

Raubenheimer, D., and S. J. Simpson. "Hunger and Satiety: Linking Mechanisms, Behaviour and Evolution." In *Encyclopedia of Animal Behaviour* 2nd ed., edited by J. C. Choe, 127–38. Amsterdam: Elsevier, 2018.

Chambers, P. G., S. J. Simpson, and D. Raubenheimer. "Behavioural Mechanisms of Nutrient Balancing in *Locusta migratoria* Nymphs," *Animal Behaviour* 50, no. 6 (1995): 1513–23.

Simpson, S. J., and P. R. White. "Associative Learning and Locust Feeding: Evidence for a 'Learned Hunger' for Protein," *Animal Behaviour* 40, no. 3 (September 1990): 506–13.

Raubenheimer, D., and D. Tucker. "Associative Learning by Locusts: Pairing of Visual Cues with Consumption of Protein and Carbohydrate," *Animal Behaviour* 54, no. 6 (December 1997): 1449–59.

Chapter 5: Seeking Exceptions to the Rule

Raubenheimer, D., and S. Jones. "Nutritional Imbalance in an Extreme Generalist Omnivore: Tolerance and Recovery Through Complementary Food Selection," *Animal Behaviour* 71, no. 6 (June 2006): 1253–62.

Mayntz, D., D. Raubenheimer, M. Salomon, S. Toft, and S. J. Simpson. "Nutrient-Specific Foraging in Invertebrate Predators," *Science* 307, no. 5706 (January 7, 2005): 111–13.

Hewson-Hughes, A. K., V. L. Hewson-Hughes, A. T. Miller, S. R. Hall, S. J. Simpson, and D. Raubenheimer. "Geometric Analysis of Macronutrient Selection in the Adult Domestic Cat, *Felis catus*," *Journal of Experimental Biology* 214 (March 15, 2011): 1039–51.

Hewson-Hughes, A. K., V. L. Hewson-Hughes, A. Colyer, A. T. Miller, S. J. McGrane, S. R. Hall, R. F. Butterwick, S. J. Simpson, and D. Raubenheimer. "Geometric Analysis of Macronutrient Selection in Breeds of the Domestic Dog, *Canis lupus familiaris*," *Behavioural Ecology* 24, no. 1 (January 2013): 293–304.

Hewson-Hughes, A. K., S. J. Simpson, and D. Raubenheimer. "Consistent Proportional Macronutrient Intake Selected by Adult Domestic Cats (*Felis catus*) Despite Variations in Dietary Macronutrient and Moisture Content of Foods Offered," *Journal of Comparative Physiology B* 183, no. 4 (May 2013): 525–36.

Hewson-Hughes, A. K., A. Colyer, S. J. Simpson, and D. Raubenheimer. "Balancing Macronutrient Intake in a Mammalian Carnivore: Disentangling the Influences of Flavour and Nutrition," *Royal Society Open Science* 3, no. 6 (June 15, 2016): 160081.

Raubenheimer, D., D. Mayntz, S. J. Simpson, and S. Toft. "Nutrient Specific Compensation Following Overwintering Diapause in a Generalist Predatory Invertebrate: Implications for Intraguild Predations," *Ecology* 88, no. 10 (October 2007): 2598–2608.

Chapter 6: The Protein Leverage Hypothesis

Simpson, S. J., R. Batley, and D. Raubenheimer. "Geometric Analysis of Macronutrient Intake in Humans: The Power of Protein?" *Appetite* 41, no. 2 (October 2003): 123–40.

Simpson, S. J., and D. Raubenheimer. "Obesity: The Protein Leverage Hypothesis," *Obesity Reviews* 6, no. 2 (May 2005): 133–42.

Gosby, A. K., A. D. Conigrave, N. S. Lau, M. A. Iglesias, R. M. Hall, S. A. Jebb, J. Brand-Miller, I. D. Caterson, D. Raubenheimer, and S. J. Simpson. "Testing Protein Leverage in Lean Humans: A Randomised Controlled Experimental Study," *PLoS ONE* 6, no. 10 (2011): e25929.

Raubenheimer D., and S. J. Simpson. "Nutritional Ecology and Human Health," *Annual Review of Nutrition* 36 (2016): 603–26.

Gosby, A. K., A. D. Conigrave, D. Raubenheimer, and S. J. Simpson. "Protein Leverage and Energy Intake," *Obesity Reviews* 15, no. 3 (March 2014): 183–91.

Raubenheimer, D., and S. J. Simpson. "Protein Leverage: Theoretical Foundations and Ten Points of Clarification," *Obesity* 27, no. 8 (August 2019): 1225–38.

Campbell, C., D. Raubenheimer, A. Badaloo, P. D. Gluckman, C. Martinez, A. K. Gosby, S. J. Simpson, C. Osmond, M. Boyne, and T. Forrester. "Developmental Contributions to Macronutrient Selection: A Randomized Controlled Trial in Adult Survivors of Malnutrition," *Evolution, Medicine, and Public Health* 2016, no. 1 (May 18, 2016): 158–69.

Chapter 7: Why Not Just Eat More Protein?

Simpson, S. J., and D. Raubenheimer. "Caloric Restriction and Aging Revisited: The Need for a Geometric Analysis of the Nutritional Bases of Aging," *Journals of Gerontology, Series A* 62, no. 7 (July 2007): 707–13.

Lee, K. P., S. J. Simpson, F. J. Clissold, R. Brooks, J. W. O. Ballard, P. W. Taylor, N. Soran, and D. Raubenheimer. "Lifespan and Reproduction in *Drosophila*: New Insights from Nutritional Geometry," *Proceedings of the National Academy of Sciences of the United States of America* 105, no. 7 (February 19, 2008): 2498–503.

Mittendorfer, B., S. Klein, and L. Fontana. "A Word of Caution against Excessive Protein Intake," *Nature Reviews Endocrinology* (November 14, 2019): doi:10.1038/s41574-019-0274-7.

Chapter 8: Mapping Nutrition

Solon-Biet, S. M., A. C. McMahon, J. W. O. Ballard, K. Ruohonen, L. E. Wu, V. C. Cogger, A. Warren, et al. "The Ratio of Macronutrients, Not Caloric Intake, Dictates Cardiometabolic Health, Aging and Longevity in *ad libitum*-fed Mice," *Cell Metabolism* 19, no. 3 (March 4, 2014): 418–30.

Gokarn, R., S. Solon-Biet, N. A. Youngson, D. Wahl, V. C. Cogger, A. C. McMahon, G. J. Cooney, et al. "The Relationship Between Dietary Macronutrients and Hepatic Telomere Length in Aging Mice," *Journals of Gerontology: Series A* 73, no. 4 (March 14, 2018): 446–49.

Di Francesco, A., C. Di Germanio, M. Bernier, and R. de Cabo. "A Time to Fast," *Science* 362, no. 6416 (November 16, 2018): 770–75.

Solon-Biet, S. M., V. C. Cogger, M. Heblinski, T. Pulpitel, D. Wahl, A. C. McMahon, A. Warren, et al. "Defining the Nutritional and

Metabolic Context of FGF21 Using the Geometric Framework," *Cell Metabolism* 24, no. 4 (October 11, 2016): 555–65.

Gosby, A. K., N. S. Lau, C. S. Tam, M. A. Iglesias, C. Morrison, I. D. Caterson, J. Brand-Miller, A. D. Conigrave, D. Raubenheimer, and S. J. Simpson. "Raised FGF-21 and Triglycerides Accompany Increased Energy Intake Driven by Protein Leverage in Lean, Healthy Individuals: A Randomised Trial," *PLoS One* 11, no. 8 (August 18, 2016): e0161003.

Hill, C. M., T. Laeger, M. Dehner, D. C. Albarado, B. Clarke, D. Wanders, S. J. Burke, et al. "FGF21 Signals Protein Status to the Brain and Adaptively Regulates Food Choice and Metabolism," *Cell Reports* 27, no.10 (4 June, 2019): 2934-2947.e3.

Le Couteur, D. G., S. Solon-Biet, D. Wahl, V. C. Cogger, B. J. Willcox, D. C. Willcox, D. Raubenheimer, and S. J. Simpson. "New Horizons: Dietary Protein, Ageing and the Okinawan Ratio," *Age and Ageing* 45, no. 4 (July 2016): 443–47.

Kaplan, H., R. C. Thompson, B. C. Trumble, L. S. Wann, A. H. Allam, B. Beheim, B. Frohlich, et al. "Coronary Atherosclerosis in Indigenous South American Tsimane: A Cross-Sectional Cohort Study," *The Lancet* 389, no. 10080 (April 29, 2017): 1730–39.

Le Couteur, D. G., S. Solon-Biet, V. C. Cogger, S. J. Mitchell, A. Senior, R. de Cabo, D. Raubenheimer, and S. J. Simpson. "The Impact of Low-Protein, High-Carbohydrate Diets on Aging and Lifespan," *Cellular and Molecular Life Sciences* 73, no. 6 (March 2016): 1237–52.

Kitada, M., Y. Ogura, I. Monno, and D. Koya. "The Impact of Dietary Protein Intake on Longevity and Metabolic Health," *EBioMedicine* (May 2019). doi: 10.1016/j.ebiom.2019.04.005.

Green, C. L., and D. W. Lamming. "Regulation of Metabolic Health by Essential Dietary Amino Acids," *Mechanisms of Ageing and Development* 177 (January 2019): 186–200.

Brandhorst, S., and V. D. Longo. "Protein Quantity and Source, Fasting-Mimicking Diets, and Longevity," *Advances in Nutrition* 10, Issue Supplement (November 4, 2019): S340-50.

Chapter 9: Food Environments

Raubenheimer, D., and E. A. Bernays. "Patterns of Feeding in the Polyphagous Grasshopper *Taeniopoda eques*: A Field Study," *Animal Behaviour* 45, no. 1 (January 1993): 153–67.

Felton, A. M., A. Felton, D. Raubenheimer, S. J. Simpson, W. J. Foley, J. T. Wood, I. R. Wallis, and D. B. Lindenmayer. "Protein Content of Diets Dictates the Daily Energy Intake of a Free-Ranging Primate," *Behavioural Ecology* 20, no. 4 (July-August 2009): 685–90.

Felton, A. M., A. Felton, J. T. Wood, W. J. Foley, D. Raubenheimer, I. R. Wallis, and D. B. Lindemayer. "Nutritional Ecology of Spider Monkeys (*Ateles chamek*) in Lowland Bolivia: How Macro-Nutrient Balancing Influences Food Choice," *International Journal of Primatology* 30, no. 5 (October 2009): 675–96.

Rothman, J. M., D. Raubenheimer, and C. A. Chapman. "Nutritional Geometry: Gorillas Prioritise Non-Protein Energy While Consuming Surplus Protein," *Biology Letters* 7, no. 6 (December 23, 2011): 847–49.

Thompson, M. E., and C. D. Knott. "Urinary C-peptide of Insulin as a Non-invasive Marker of Energy Balance in Wild Orangutans," *Hormones and Behavior* 53, no. 4 (April 2008): 526–35.

Vogel, E. R., J. M. Rothman, A. M. Moldawer, T. D. Bransford, M. E. Emery-Thompson, M. A. Van Noordwijk, S. S. Utami Atomoko, B. E. Crowley, C. D. Knott, W. M. Erb, and D. Raubenheimer. "Coping with a Challenging Environment: Nutritional Balancing, Health, and Energetics in Wild Bornean Orangutans," *American Journal of Physical Anthropology* 156 (2015): 314–15.

Chapter 10: Changing Food Environments

Qiu, Q., L. Z. Wang, K. Wang, Y. Z. Yang, T. Ma, Z. F. Wang, et al. "Yak Whole-Genome Resequencing Reveals Domestication Signatures and Prehistoric Population Expansions," *Nature Communications* (2015): 6.

Wangchuk, D., W. Dhammasaccakarn, P. Tepsing, and T. P. N. Sakolnakarn. "The Yaks: Heart and Soul of the Himalayan Tribes of Bhutan," *Journal of Environmental Research and Management* 4, no. 2 (2013): 189–96.

Raubenheimer, D., and J. M. Rothman. "The Nutritional Ecology of Entomophagy in Humans and Other Primates," *Annual Review of Entomology.* 58 (2013): 141–60.

Raubenheimer, D., J. M. Rothman, H. Pontzer, and S. J. Simpson. "Macronutrient Contributions of Insects to the Diets of Hunter-gatherers: A Geometric Analysis," *Journal of Human Evolution* 71 (2014): 70–76.

Wrangham, R. *Catching Fire: How Cooking Made Us Human.* London: Profile Books Ltd., 2010.

Pontzer, H., B. M. Wood, and D. A. Raichlen. "Hunter-gatherers as Models in Public Health," *Obesity Reviews* 19 (2018): 24–35.

Arendt, M., K. M. Cairns, J. W. O. Ballard, P. Savolainen, and E. Axelsson. "Diet Adaptation in Dog Reflects Spread of Prehistoric Agriculture," *Heredity* 117, no. 5 (November 2016): 301–6.

Beja-Pereira, A., G. Luikart, P. R. England, D. G. Bradley, O. C. Jann, G. Bertorelle, et al. "Gene-Culture Coevolution Between Cattle Milk Protein Genes and Human Lactase Genes," *Nature Genetics* 35 (2003): 311–13.

Kemp, C. "Evolution's Traps: When Our World Leads Animals Astray," *New Scientist* (March 12, 2014).

Monteiro, C. A., J. C. Moubarac, G. Cannon, S. W. Ng, and B. Popkin. "Ultra-Processed Products Are Becoming Dominant in the Global Food System," *Obesity Reviews* 14, no. S2 (November 2013): S21–28.

Chapter 11: Modern Environments

Moss, M. *Salt, Sugar, Fat: How the Food Giants Hooked Us.* New York: Random House, 2013.

Monteiro, C. A., G. Cannon, R. B. Levy, J. C. Moubarac, M. L. C. Louzada, F. Rauber, N. Khandpur, et al. "Ultra-Processed Foods: What They Are and How to Identify Them," *Public Health Nutrition* 22, no. 5 (April 2019): 936–41.

Martínez Steele, E., D. Raubenheimer, S. J. Simpson, L. Baraldi, and C. Monteiro. "Ultra-processed Foods, Protein Leverage and Energy Intake in the USA," *Public Health Nutrition* 21, Special Issue no. 1 (January 2018): 114–24.

Brooks, R. C., S. J. Simpson, and D. Raubenheimer. "The Price of Protein: Combining Evolutionary and Economic Analysis to Understand Excessive Energy Consumption," *Obesity Reviews* 11, no. 12 (December 2010): 887–94.

Raubenheimer, D., G. E. Machovsky-Capuska, A. K. Gosby, and S. Simpson. "Nutritional Ecology of Obesity: From Humans to Companion Animals," *British Journal of Nutrition* 113, no. S1 (January 2015): S26–39.

Zhu, C. W., K. Kobayashi, I. Loladze, J. G. Zhu, Q. Jiang, X. Xu, G. Liu, S. Seneweera, K. L. Ebi, A. Drewnowski, et al. "Carbon Dioxide (CO_2) Levels This Century Will Alter the Protein, Micronutrients, and Vitamin Content of Rice Grains with Potential Health Consequences for the Poorest Rice-Dependent Countries," *Science Advances* 4, no. 5 (May 23, 2018): eaaq1012.

Chapter 12: A Unique Appetite

Nestle, M. *Food Politics: How the Food Industry Influences Nutrition and Health.* Berkeley, CA: University of California Press, 2002.

Nestle, M. *Unsavory Truth: How Food Companies Skew the Science of What We Eat.* New York: Basic Books, 2018.

Scrinis, G. *Nutritionism: The Science and Politics of Dietary Advice.* New York: Columbia University Press, 2013.

Orskes, N., and E. M. Conway. *Merchants of Doubt: How a Handful of Scientists Obscured the Truth on Issues from Tobacco Smoke to Global Warming.* London: Bloomsbury, 2011.

Brownbill, A. L., C. L. Miller, and A. J. Braunack-Mayer. "Industry Use of 'Better-for-You' Features on Labels of Sugar-Containing Beverages," *Public Health Nutrition* 21, no. 18 (December 2018): 3335–43.

Simpson, S. J., and D. Raubenheimer. "Perspective: Tricks of the Trade," *Nature* 508 (April 17, 2014): S66.

Brownell, K.D., and K. E. Warner. "The Perils of Ignoring History: Big Tobacco Played Dirty and Millions Died. How Similar Is Big Food?" *Milbank Quarterly* 87 (2009): 259–94.

Schuldt, J. P., 2013. "Does Green Mean Healthy? Nutrition Label Color Affects Perceptions of Healthfulness." *Health Communication* 28: 814–21.

"New Archive Reveals How the Food Industry Mimics Big Tobacco to Suppress Science, Shape Public Opinion." https://civileats.com/2018/11/28/new-archive-reveals-how-the-food-industry-mimics-big-tobacc-to-suppress-science-shape-public-opinion/

"The Food Industrial Complex." https://priceonomics.com/the-food-industrial-complex/

Moodie, R., D. Stuckler, C. Monteiro, N. Sheron, B. Neal, T. Thamarangsi, P. Lincoln, and S. Casswell on behalf of *The Lancet* NCD Action Group. "Profits and Pandemics: Prevention of Harmful Effects of Tobacco, Alcohol, and Ultra-Processed Food and Drink Industries," *Lancet* 381, no. 9867 (February 23, 2013): 670–79.

Lesser, L. I., C. B. Ebbeling, M. Goozner, D. Wypij, and D. S. Ludwig. "Relationship between Funding Source and Conclusion among Nutrition-related Scientific Articles," *PLoS Medicine* 4 (2007): 41–46.

Chapter 13: Moving the Protein Target and a Vicious Cycle to Obesity

Blumfield, M. L., C. Nowson, A. J. Hure, R. Smith, S. J. Simpson, D. Raubenheimer, L. MacDonald-Wicks, and C. E. Collins. "Lower Protein-to-Carbohydrate Ratio in Maternal Diet Is Associated with Higher Childhood Systolic Blood Pressure Up to Age Four Years," *Nutrients* 7, no. 5 (April 24, 2015): 3078–93.

Blumfield, M. L., A. J. Hure, L. K. MacDonald-Wicks, R. Smith, S. J. Simpson, W. B. Giles, D. Raubenheimer, and C. E. Collins. "Dietary Balance During Pregnancy Predicts Fetal Adiposity and Fat Distribution," *American Journal of Clinical Nutrition* 96, no. 5 (November 2012): 1032–41.

Blumfield, M., A. Hure, L. MacDonald-Wicks, R. Smith, S. J. Simpson, D. Raubenheimer, and C. Collins. "The Association Between the Macronutrient Content of Maternal Diet and the Adequacy of Micronutrients During Pregnancy in the Women and Their Children's Health (WATCH) Study," *Nutrients* 4, no. 12 (December 2012): 1958–76.

Saner, C., D. Tassoni, B. E. Harcourt, K-T Kao, E. J. Alexander, Z. McCallum, T. Olds, et al. "Evidence for the Protein Leverage Hypothesis in Obese Children and Adolescents" (forthcoming).

Weber, M., V. Grote, R. Closa-Monasterolo, J. Escribano, J. P. Langhendries, E. Dain, M. Giovannini, European Childhood Obesity Trial Study Group, et al. "Lower Protein Content in Infant Formula Reduces BMI and Obesity Risk at School Age: Follow-Up of a Randomized Trial," *American Journal of Clinical Nutrition* 99, no. 5 (May 2014): 1041–51.

Senior, A. M., S. M. Solon-Biet, V. C. Cogger, D. G. Le Couteur, S. Nakagawa, D. Raubenheimer, and S. J. Simpson. "Dietary Macronutrient Content, Age-Specific Mortality and Lifespan," *Proceedings of the Royal Society B* 286, no. 1902 (May 15, 2019): 20190393.

Levine, M. E., J. A. Suarez, S. Brandhorst, P. Balasubramanian, C. W. Cheng, F. Madia, L. Fontana, et al. "Low Protein Intake Is Associated with a Major Reduction in IGF-1, Cancer, and Overall Mortality in the 65 and Younger But Not Older Population," *Cell Metabolism* 19, no. 3 (March 4, 2014): 407–17.

Wu, G. "Dietary Protein Intake and Human Health," *Food & Function* 7, no. 3 (March 2016): 1251–65.

Katz, D. L., K. N. Doughty, K. Geagan, D. A. Jenkins, and C. D. Gardner. "Perspective: The Public Health Case for Modernizing the Definition of Protein Quality," *Advances in Nutrition* 10, no. 5 (September 1, 2019): 755–64. doi: 10.1093/advances/nmz023.

Chapter 14: Putting Lessons into Practice

Larsen, T. M., S.-M. Dalskov, M. van Baak, S. A. Jebb, A. Papadaki, A. F. H. Pfeiffer, J. A. Martinez, et al. for the Diet, Obesity, and Genes (Diogenes) Project. "Diets with High or Low Protein Content and Glycemic Index for Weight-Loss Maintenance," *New England Journal of Medicine* 363, no. 22 (November 25, 2011): 2102–13.

Monteiro, C. A., G. Cannon, R. B. Levy, J. C. Moubarac, M. L. C. Louzada, F. Rauber, N. Khandpur, et al. "Ultra-Processed Foods: What They Are and How to Identify Them," *Public Health Nutrition* 22, no. 5 (April 2019): 936–41.

Monteiro, C. A., G. Cannon, J. C. Moubarac, A. P. B. Martins, C. A. Martins, J. Garzillo, D. S. Canella, et al. "Dietary Guidelines to Nourish Humanity and the Planet in the Twenty-First Century:

A Blueprint from Brazil," *Public Health Nutrition* 18, no. 13 (September 2015): 2311–22.

Sluik, D., E. M. Brouwer-Brolsma, A. A. M. Berendsen, V. Mikkilä, S. D. Poppitt, M. P. Silvestre, A. Tremblay, et al. "Protein Intake and the Incidence of Pre-Diabetes and Diabetes in 4 Population-Based Studies: The PREVIEW Project," *American Journal of Clinical Nutrition* 109, no. 5 (May 3, 2019): 1310–18.

Solon-Biet, S. M., V. C. Cogger, T. Pultipel, D. Wahl, X. Clark, E. Bagley, G. C. Gregoriou, et al. "Branched-Chain Amino Acids Impact Health and Lifespan Indirectly via Amino Acid Balance and Appetite Control," *Nature Metabolism* 1 (2019): 532–45. doi: 10.1038/s42255-019-0059-2.

Seidelmann, S. B., B. Claggett, S. Cheng, M. Henglin, A. Shah, L. M. Steffen, A. R. Folsom, E. B. Rimm, W. C. Willett, and S. D. Solomon. "Dietary Carbohydrate Intake and Mortality: A Prospective Cohort Study and Meta-analysis," *Lancet Public Health* 3 (2018): E419-E428.

Mazidi, M., N. Katsiki, D. P. Mikhailidis, N. Sattar, and M. Banach, on behalf of the International Lipid Expert Panel (ILEP) and the Lipid and Blood Pressure Meta-analysis Collaboration (LBPMC) Group. "Lower Carbohydrate Diets and All-cause and Cause-specific Mortality: A Population-based Cohort Study and Pooling of Prospective Studies," *European Heart Journal* 40 (2019): 2870–2879. https://doi.org/10.1093/eurheartj/ehz174

Index

NOTE: Page references in *italics* refer to figures and tables.

K

L

M